To Ross.
Xmas 1996
Love, Stuart & Kay
xxx

THE KINGFISHER Nursery COLLECTION

This edition produced for
The Book People Ltd., Guardian House,
Borough Road, Godalming, Surrey GU7 2AE

First published in 1993 by Kingfisher Books

Some of the material in this edition was previously
published by Kingfisher Books in: *The Kingfisher
Nursery Treasury* 1988, *The Kingfisher Treasury of
Nursery Stories* 1990, *The Kingfisher Nursery Songbook* 1991
and *The Kingfisher Nursery Treasure Chest* 1991

BRITISH LIBRARY CATALOGUING IN PUBLICATION DATA
A catalogue record for this book is available
from the British Library

ISBN 1 85697 045 0

Printed in Italy

THE KINGFISHER

Nursery COLLECTION

SELECTED BY

SALLY EMERSON

STORIES RETOLD BY

SUSAN PRICE

ILLUSTRATED BY

COLIN & MOIRA MACLEAN

TED SMART

CONTENTS

Baby Games 10

A selection of playsongs for babies and toddlers. There are tickle, touch and rocking rhymes, knee rides and bouncers, as well as finger games and simple action songs.

First Stories 32

Goldilocks and the Three Bears • The Three Little Pigs • The Gingerbread Man • The Little Red Hen

Nursery Songs 64

Favourite nursery rhymes for you to read and sing to your children.

Animal Tales 90

The Three Billy Goats Gruff • The Lion and the Mouse • The House on the Hill • Brer Rabbit and the Tar Baby • The Town Mouse and the Country Mouse • The Hare and the Tortoise

Dancing and Singing Games 118

Jumping, clapping, hopping, miming and marching songs, as well as traditional children's games to sing and play.

Magical Tales 142

The Magic Porridge Pot • The Princess and the Pea • The Enormous Turnip • Jack and the Beanstalk

A was an Apple Pie 166

Delightful rhymes to introduce the letters of the alphabet, numbers, days of the week and months of the year. There are memory rhymes and wise old sayings too.

Story Rhymes 184

Well-loved nursery characters appear in fantastical, funny and familiar story rhymes.

Bedtime Stories 202

The Frog Prince • The Elves and the Shoemaker
Little Red Riding Hood • Rumpelstiltskin

Lullabies 232

Enchanting poems and songs to lull children to sleep. Ideal for the end of the day.

Index of Rhymes 250

BABY GAMES

Here sits Farmer Giles *12*
Knock at the door *14*
Can you keep a secret? *14*
Here are the lady's knives and forks *15*
Dance, Thumbkin, dance *16*
Two little dicky birds *16*
This little cow eats grass *17*
Wee Wiggie *17*
This pig got into the barn *18*
This little pig went to market *19*
Pat-a-cake, pat-a-cake *20*
Handy Pandy *20*
Hob, shoe, hob *21*
Leg over leg *21*
Father and Mother and Uncle John *22*
This is the way the ladies ride *23*
Jelly on the plate *24*
Dance to your daddy *25*
Rigadoon, rigadoon *25*
The elephant goes *26*
Here is a ball for baby *26*
Round and round the garden *27*
Ring-a-ring o' roses *28*
What shall we do with a lazy Katie? *29*
Jack-in-the-box *30*
Ride a cock-horse *31*
Rock, rock, rock your boat *31*
A trot, a canter *31*

Here sits Farmer Giles,

☆ *Touch his forehead.*

Here sit his two men,

☆ *Touch his eyes.*

Here sits the
cockadoodle,

☆ *Touch his nose.*

Here sits the hen,
☆ *Touch his lips.*

Here sit the little chickens,
☆ *Touch his teeth.*

Here they run in,
Chin chopper,
Chin chopper,
Chin, chin, chin.
☆ *Tickle his chin.*

1

Knock at the door,

☆ *Tap her forehead.*

2

Ring the bell,

☆ *Tug her hair.*

3

Lift the latch,

☆ *Tweak her nose.*

4

And walk in.

☆ *Walk your fingers on her lips.*

Can you keep a secret?
I wonder if you can.
Don't laugh and don't cry
While it tickles in your hand.

Here are the lady's
knives and forks,

☆ *Hands back to back, intertwine fingers.*

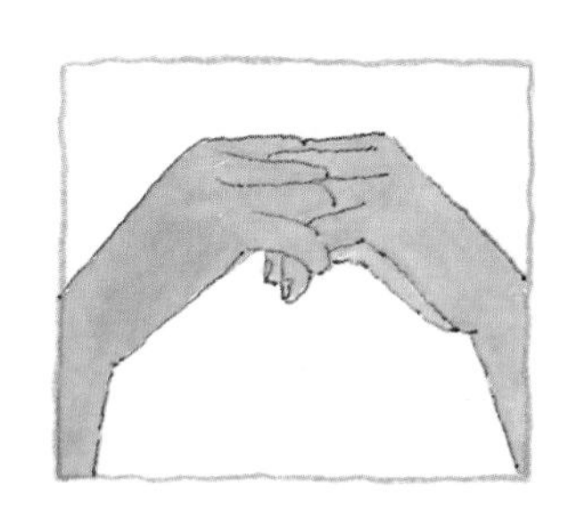

Here's the lady's
table,

☆ *Turn hands over.*

Here's the lady's
looking-glass,

☆ *Raise little fingers.*

And here's the
baby's cradle.
Rock-rock,
rock-rock, rock.

☆ *Raise index fingers and rock.*

Dance, Thumbkin, dance,
Dance, you merry men, every one;
But Thumbkin, he can dance alone,
Thumbkin, he can dance.

☆ *Waggle thumb on its own, tucking the four fingers into palm; then waggle all fingers; then the thumb on its own again. Repeat the game with each finger.*

Dance, Pointer, dance . . .
Dance, Longman, dance . . .
Dance, Ringman, dance . . .
Dance, Baby, dance . . .

1

Two little dicky birds,
Sitting on a wall,

2

One named Peter,
One named Paul.

3

Fly away, Peter!

4

Fly away, Paul!

5

Come back, Peter!
Come back, Paul!

This little cow eats grass,
This little cow eats hay,
This little cow looks over
the hedge,
This little cow runs away.
And this BIG cow does
nothing at all
But lie in the fields all day!
We'll chase her.
And chase her.
And chase her!

☆ *A finger-counting rhyme, starting at the little finger. End by pouncing on the thumb.*

Wee Wiggie,
Poke Piggie,
Tom Whistle,
John Gristle
And old BIG GOBBLE,
gobble, gobble!

☆ *A toe-counting rhyme. Start with the little toe and end by seizing the big toe and pretending to gobble it up.*

This pig got into
the barn,
☆ *Starts at the big toe.*

This ate all
the corn,

This said he
wasn't well,

This said he'd go
and tell,

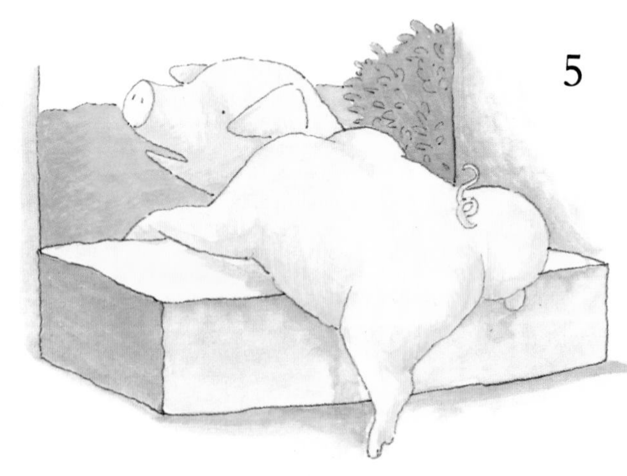

And this said: Squeak! squeak! squeak!
I can't get over the barn door sill.

This little pig went to market,
This little pig stayed at home,
This little pig had roast beef,
This little pig had none,
And this little pig cried:
Wee-wee-wee-wee-wee-wee,
All the way home!

☆ *An old favourite – count from big to little toe and end with a tickle.*

Pat-a-cake, pat-a-cake, baker's man,
Bake me a cake as fast as you can;
Pat it and prick it and mark it with B,
Put it in the oven for baby and me.

☆ *A hand-patting rhyme for babies and a first clapping song for toddlers. Act out the rhyme by pretending to prick the baby's palm and tracing a B on it.*

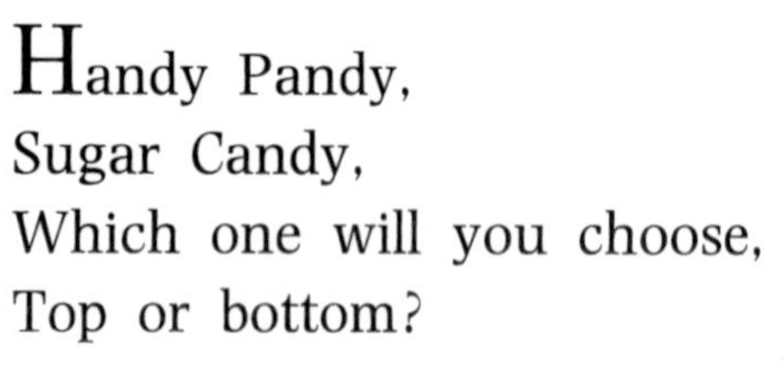

Handy Pandy,
Sugar Candy,
Which one will you choose,
Top or bottom?

☆ *Hide something in one hand. Then put one closed fist over the other. The game is to choose the right hand.*

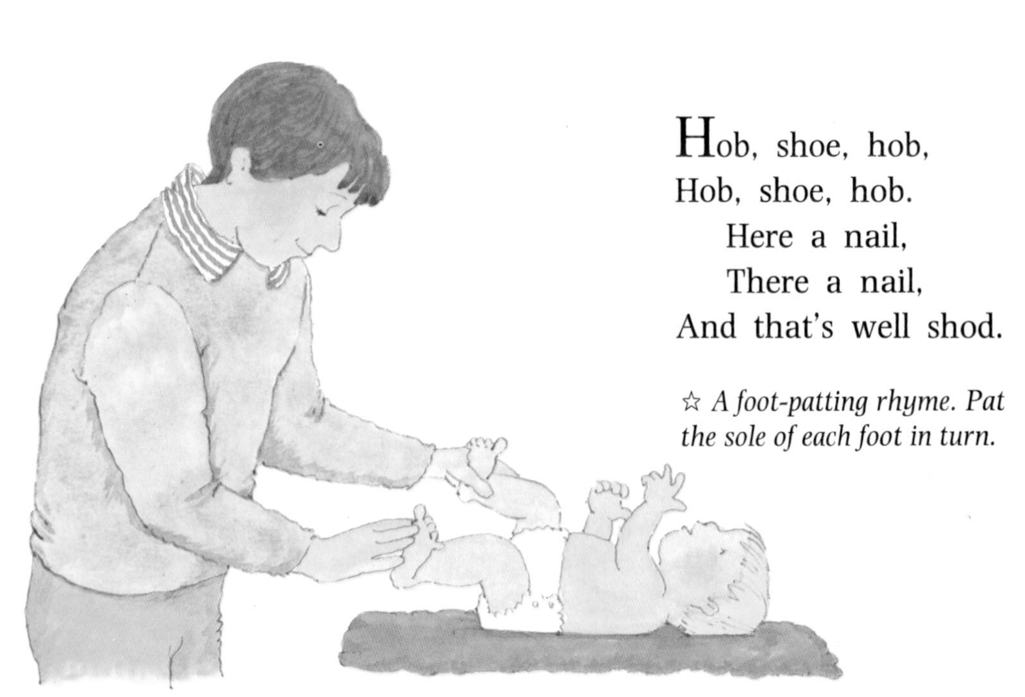

Hob, shoe, hob,
Hob, shoe, hob.
Here a nail,
There a nail,
And that's well shod.

☆ *A foot-patting rhyme. Pat the sole of each foot in turn.*

Leg over leg,
As the dog goes to Dover,
When he comes to a wall,
Jump! He goes over!

☆ *Sit the baby in your lap with his back to you. Cross and uncross his legs in time to the first three lines. At JUMP lift both legs up so that he topples back into you.*

1

Father and Mother and Uncle John
Went to market, one by one,
☆ *Jog the baby gently.*

2

Father fell off!
☆ *Drop her to one side.*

3

Mother fell off!
☆ *Drop her to the other side.*

4

But Uncle John went on, and on,
And on, and on and on.
☆ *Now bounce faster and faster.*

This is the way the ladies ride,
Nimble-nim, nimble-nim;

This is the way the gentlemen ride,
Gallop-a-trot! Gallop-a-trot!

This is the way the farmers ride,
Jiggety-jog, jiggety-jog;

This is the way the butcher boy rides,
Tripperty-trot, tripperty-trot,

Till he falls in a ditch with a flipperty,
Flipperty, flop, flop, FLOP!

☆ *This knee ride gets faster and faster. End with a sudden drop between your knees.*

Jelly on the plate,
Jelly on the plate,
Wibble wobble,
Wibble wobble,
Jelly on the plate.

☆ *Wobble from side to side.*

Sweeties in the jar,
Sweeties in the jar,
Shake them up,
Shake them up,
Sweeties in the jar.

☆ *Shake up and down.*

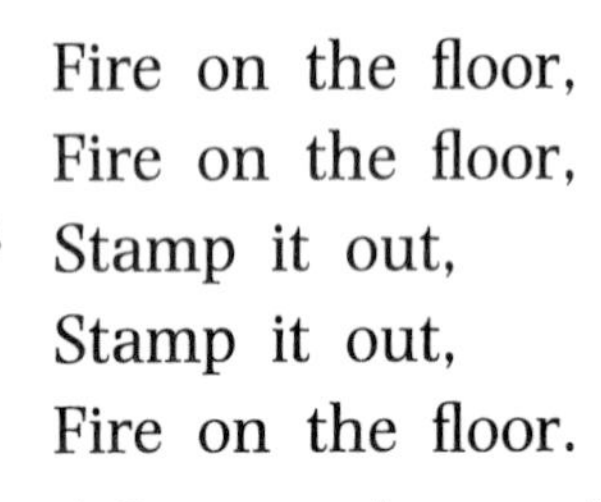

Fire on the floor,
Fire on the floor,
Stamp it out,
Stamp it out,
Fire on the floor.

☆ *Bounce to the ground and up.*

Candles on the cake,
Candles on the cake,
Blow them out,
Blow them out,
Puff puff puff.

☆ *Blow each other gently.*

☆ *A bouncing rhyme.*

Dance to your daddy,
My little babby,
Dance to your daddy,
My little lamb.

You shall have a fishy,
In a little dishy,
You shall have a fishy,
When the boat comes in.

Rigadoon, rigadoon,
Now let him fly,
Sit him on father's foot,
Jump him up high.

☆ *Cross your legs and sit the baby on your crossed ankle. Swing up and down.*

☆ Toddlers will enjoy acting out this rhyme.

The elephant goes
like this, like that,

He's terribly big,

And he's terribly fat.

He has no fingers,

He has no toes,

But goodness, gracious,
what a nose!

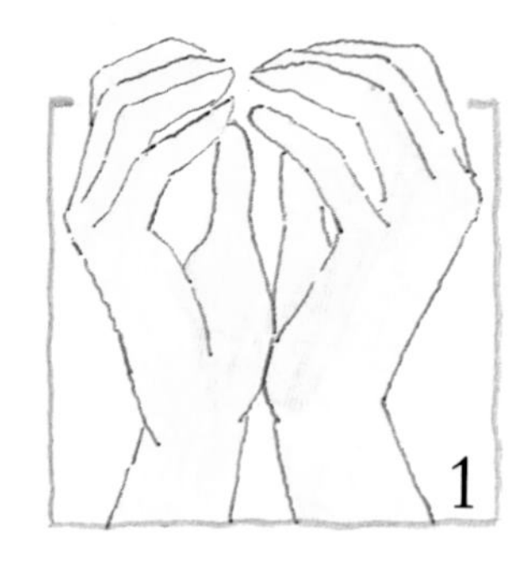

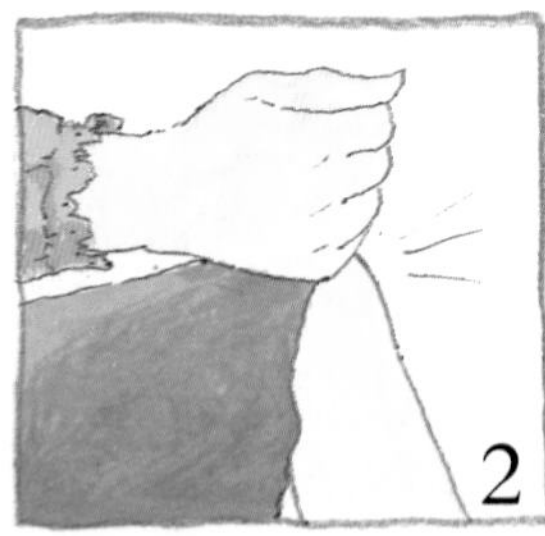

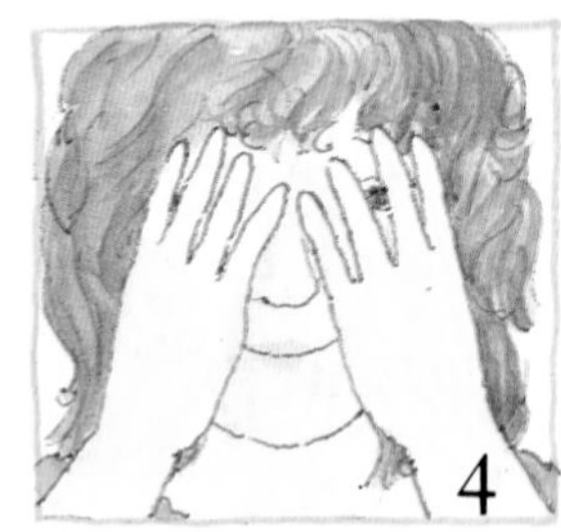

Here is a ball
for baby,
Big and soft
and round.

Here is a baby's
hammer,
See how it can
pound.

Here is a baby's
trumpet,
Tootle tootle
toot.

Here is the way
my baby
Plays peek-a-boo,
Boo!

Round and round the garden
Like a teddy bear.
One step, two step,
Tickle you under there!

Ring-a-ring o' roses,
A pocket full of posies,
A-tishoo! A-tishoo!
We all fall down.

☆ *Choose either of the two second verses to start again. Older children will love the race in the second version.*

The cows are in the meadow,
Eating buttercups,
A-tishoo! A-tishoo!
We all get up.

The cows are in the meadow,
Eating all the grass,
A-tishoo! A-tishoo!
Who's up last?
NOT ME!

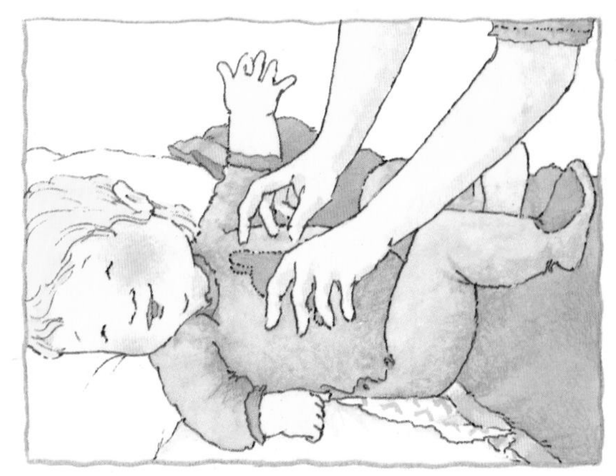

What shall we do with
a lazy Katie?
What shall we do with
a lazy Katie?
What shall we do with
a lazy Katie,
Early in the morning?

Roll her on the bed and
tickle her all over,
Roll her on the bed and
tickle her all over,
Roll her on the bed and
tickle her all over,
Early in the morning.

Heave
ho
and UP
she rises,

Heave ho and UP she rises,
Heave ho and UP she rises,
Early in the morning.

♫ *Sing to the tune of "What shall we do with the drunken sailor?"*

Jack-in-the-box jumps UP
like this,
☆ *Swing him up high.*

He makes me laugh when he
waggles his head,
☆ *Shake him gently.*

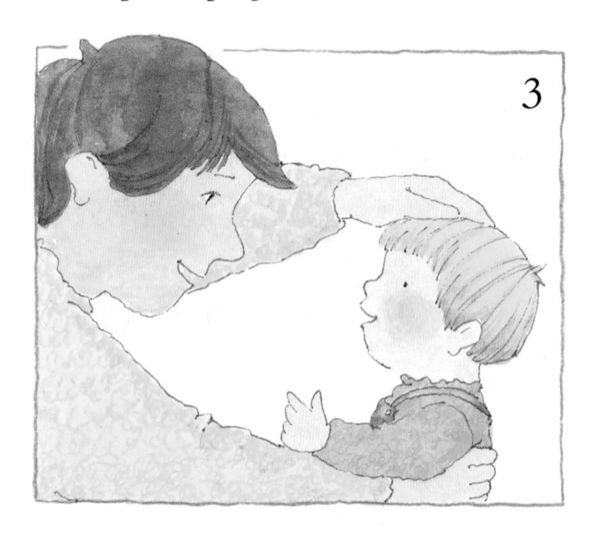

I gently press him
down again,
☆ *Lower him down.*

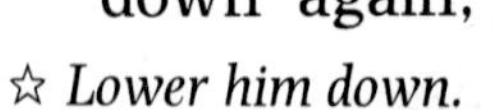

But Jack-in-the-box
jumps UP instead.
☆ *Swing him up again.*

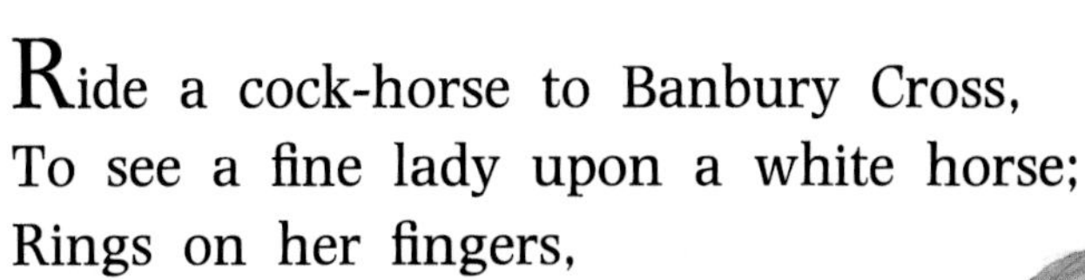

Ride a cock-horse to Banbury Cross,
To see a fine lady upon a white horse;
Rings on her fingers,
And bells on her toes,
She shall have music
wherever she goes.

Rock, rock, rock your boat,
Gently down the stream,
Merrily, merrily, merrily, merrily,
Life is but a dream.

☆ *Rock small babies from side to side. Pull older ones up to sitting position and back again.*

A trot, a canter,
A gallop and over,
Out of the saddle
And roll in the clover.

☆ *One last knee ride. End by swinging the baby right out of the "saddle" down to the ground.*

FIRST STORIES

Goldilocks and the Three Bears
35

The Three Little Pigs
42

The Gingerbread Man
51

The Little Red Hen
59

Goldilocks and the Three Bears

Once upon a time, in a little house that was built in a deep, dark wood, lived three bears.

The biggest was Daddy Bear. The middling one was Mummy Bear. And the littlest one was Baby Bear.

Every morning they had porridge for breakfast. But one morning the porridge was too hot and burned their mouths.

"Let's go for a walk in the wood," said Mummy Bear, "until the porridge is cool enough to eat."

"Good idea," said Daddy Bear. So they took Baby Bear's paws in theirs and walked out into the wood.

Their little house was left empty, with three bowls of porridge cooling on the table.

Then, through the wood, came a little girl. She was lost and hungry, and her name was Goldilocks.

When Goldilocks saw the little house she thought, "Oh, I wonder who lives there? Perhaps they can tell me how to find my way out of the wood. Perhaps they can give me something to eat." So she went up to the little house and knocked at the door.

But no one answered, even when she knocked again.

She tried to look in at the window, but she wasn't tall enough. She called, but still no one came.

So she stood on tip-toe, and stretched up high, and opened the door, even though it wasn't her house! She went quietly inside and looked all around.

No one was at home. But on the table stood those three bowls of porridge: a great big bowl, a middling-sized bowl and a tiny little bowl.

"I'm so hungry," thought Goldilocks, "and there's no one here to ask. I'll just try some of this porridge."

First she went to the great big bowl. She dug in the spoon and took a big mouthful. But it was HOT!

"Too hot! Too hot!" cried Goldilocks, and she dropped the spoon back in the bowl.

Next she went to the middling-sized bowl and tried a spoonful of that. But it was sticky and COLD! Goldilocks pulled a face. "Too cold! Too cold!" she said, and she dropped that spoon back in the bowl as well.

Then she tried the porridge in the littlest bowl. It was not too hot and not too cold but just right! So she ate it all up and licked the bowl clean.

Goldilocks was feeling very tired because she'd walked so far through the wood. Looking round, she saw three chairs against the wall: a great big chair, a middling-sized chair and a tiny little chair.

First she climbed onto the great big chair. But it was too hard and she quickly slid off again.

Then Goldilocks tried the middling-sized chair. But that was too soft and she soon scrambled out.

But when she sat on the tiny little chair, it wasn't too hard and it wasn't too soft. In fact, it was just right, so she thought, "I'll sit here for a while."

But just as Goldilocks thought that, the tiny little chair broke and she fell on the floor!

When she got up she was very cross. "Stupid chair," she thought. "I'm still tired. I still want somewhere to rest." So she went upstairs, even though it wasn't her house, and found a room with three beds.

There was a great big bed, a middling-sized bed and a tiny little bed. Goldilocks tried the great big bed first, but it was too hard. So she rolled off it and tried the middling-sized bed. But that bed was too soft. So she left that one and

tried the tiny little bed.

Now the tiny little bed wasn't too hard and it wasn't too soft. In fact, it was just right! It was so comfortable that Goldilocks soon fell fast asleep.

While she was asleep, the three bears came home from their walk in the wood. They looked at their porridge bowls and Daddy Bear saw that a big spoonful had been taken from his bowl.

In his great big bear's voice, he growled, "Who's been eating my porridge?"

In her soft, middling voice, Mummy Bear said, "And who's been eating my porridge?"

In her tiny little voice, Baby Bear said, "Who's been eating my porridge and has eaten it all up?"

Then Daddy Bear saw that his chair had been moved and he roared, "Who's been sitting on my chair?" And Mummy Bear, in her middling voice, said, "Who's been sitting on my chair?" Baby Bear began to cry, "Who's been sitting on my chair and has broken it all up?"

Then the three bears went upstairs. In his great big voice, Daddy Bear said, "Who's been sleeping in my bed?" And

Mummy Bear said, "Who's been sleeping in my bed?" Then Baby Bear cried, "Who's been sleeping in my bed and is still in it?"

Mummy Bear and Daddy Bear came to look. There lay Goldilocks, snoring in the little bed. But the sound of Baby Bear crying woke her and she sat up.

When she saw three bears looking at her, she was so frightened that she jumped right out of the window. Luckily she landed in the soft grass so she wasn't hurt. Then off she ran as fast as she could. Soon she was out of the wood and was able to find her way home. Goldilocks never came back and lived happily ever after.

As for the three bears, whenever they went for a walk after that, they remembered to lock their door so no one could creep in, eat their porridge or break their chairs. So they lived happily ever after too. Everyone was happy. And that's the end.

The Three Little Pigs

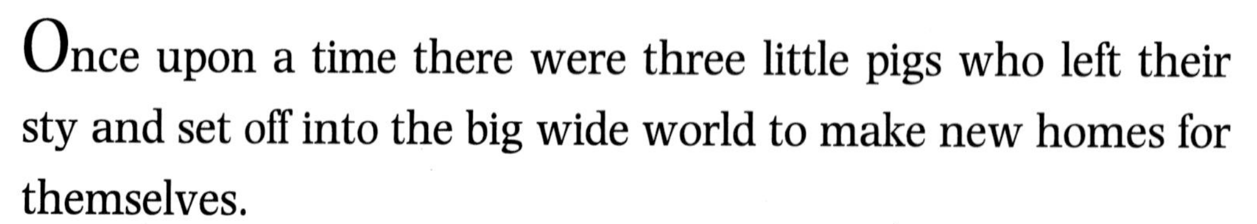

Once upon a time there were three little pigs who left their sty and set off into the big wide world to make new homes for themselves.

The first little pig was walking along the road when he met a man carrying a load of straw.

"Straw," thought the little pig. "I could easily build myself a house of straw. It wouldn't take me very long or be much trouble."

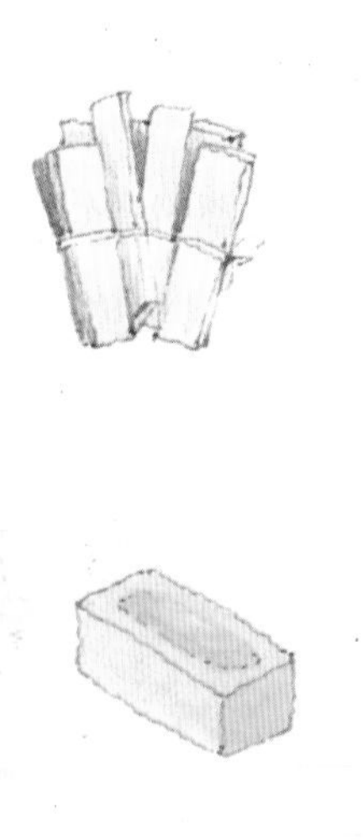

So the first little pig bought the load of straw from the man and built himself a house with it. And he lived happily in his house of straw.

The second little pig was walking along the road when he met a man carrying a load of sticks.

"Sticks," thought the little pig. "I could easily build myself a house of sticks. It wouldn't take me very long or be much trouble."

So the second little pig bought the sticks from the man and built himself a house with them. And he lived happily in his house of sticks.

The third little pig was walking along the road when he met a man with a load of bricks.

"Bricks," thought the little pig. "I could build myself a house of bricks. It would take a long time and a lot of trouble, but when it was finished, it would be a good strong house."

So the third little pig bought the bricks from the man and he set to work to build himself a brick house. It took him many weeks of mixing mortar to stick the bricks together and of laying the bricks one on top of another to make the walls. Day after day he worked away at it.

The first little pig and the second little pig often came to watch. "Look at you, working so hard!" they said. "We finished our houses long ago and now we can play."

"Yes," said the third little pig, "but my house will be drier than yours, and warmer and stronger."

But the first little pig and the second little pig didn't think that mattered. They laughed and ran away.

Then along came the big bad wolf. Wolves eat little pigs.

The big bad wolf saw the first little pig and the first little pig saw him.

Away ran the little pig and shut himself into his house of straw.

"Let me in, little pig, let me in," said the wolf.

"Oh no! Not by the hair of my chinny-chin-chin!" said the little pig. "I won't let you in."

"Then I'll huff, and I'll puff, and I'll blow your house down!" said the wolf.

And the wolf huffed, and he puffed, and he blew down the house of straw. And if the first little pig hadn't been quick, he would have been eaten. But he was quick, and he ran away to the house of sticks where his brother lived.

The two little pigs shut themselves into the house of sticks and waited. By and by the wolf came and the wolf said, "Let me in, little pigs, let me in."

"Oh no! Not by the hairs on our chinny-chin-chins! We won't let you in," said the two little pigs.

"Then I'll huff, and I'll puff, and I'll blow your house down!" said the wolf.

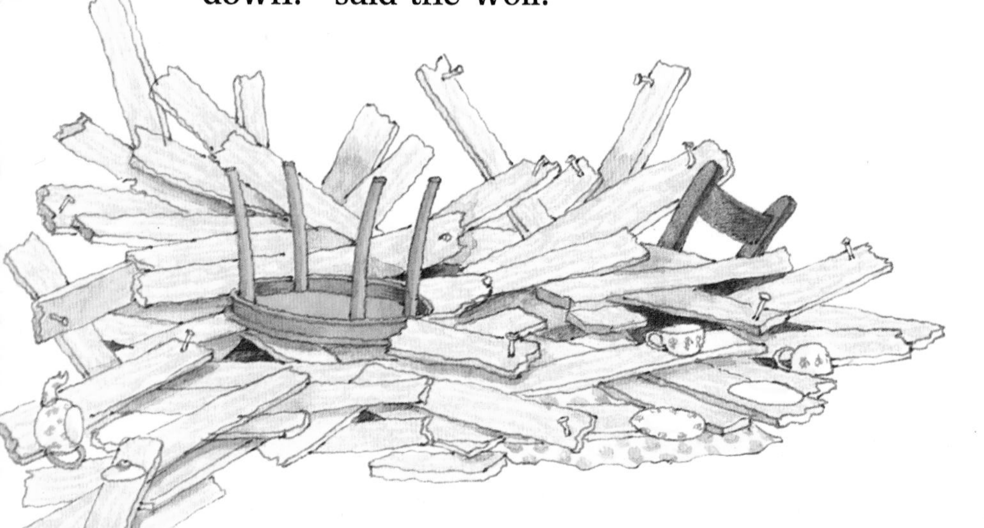

And he huffed, and he puffed, and he blew down the house of sticks. And if the two little pigs hadn't been quick, they would have been eaten. But they were quick, and they ran away to the house of bricks where their brother lived.

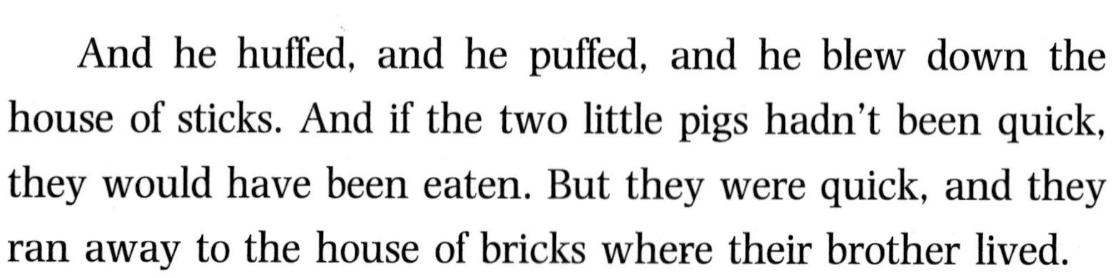

The three little pigs shut themselves into the house of bricks. By and by the wolf came and said, "Let me in, little pigs, let me in."

"Oh no! Not by the hairs on our chinny-chin-chins! We won't let you in," said the three little pigs.

"Then I'll huff, and I'll puff, and I'll blow your house down!" said the wolf.

He huffed, and he puffed – but the house of bricks didn't fall down.

So the wolf took a bigger breath and he huffed harder, and puffed harder – but the house of bricks still didn't fall down. It was stronger than straw or sticks.

So the wolf took an even deeper breath and he huffed harder still, and puffed harder still. But the house of bricks just wouldn't fall down. It was too strong.

The wolf was exhausted with huffing and puffing, and he crawled away to get his breath back.

How the first little pig and the second little pig cheered when they saw the wolf slink away! They thought that they

were safe now. But the third little pig said, "Help me to fill the cooking pot with water and light a fire under it."

So they lit a fire and hung the big cooking pot over it and then they filled the pot with water. The water was soon boiling.

"That wolf won't have given up yet," said the third little pig. "We have to be ready for him."

Now it wasn't long before the wolf got his breath back, and he wondered how he could get the little pigs. He couldn't blow down the brick house because it was too strong. He couldn't get in by the door because it was locked. He couldn't get in by the windows because they were shuttered. But there was the chimney.

So the wolf climbed up onto the roof and started to climb down the chimney to get the three little pigs.

But he landed right in the cooking pot that the three little pigs had set ready. So instead of the wolf having pig for his dinner, the three little pigs had wolf stew for theirs.

Then the first little pig and the second little pig built brick houses for themselves and they all lived happily ever after.

And that's the end of the story.

The Gingerbread Man

Once upon a time there was an old woman who was baking. She made a gingerbread man for tea. She cut him out of spicy gingerbread and gave him currants for his eyes and mouth, and currant buttons down his front. Then she put him in the oven to bake.

A little while later there was a knock at the door. Not the kitchen door – the oven door! A voice shouted, "Let me out! Let me out!"

So the old woman opened the oven door and *whoosh!* the gingerbread man raced past her, across the kitchen floor and out into the garden. The old woman ran after him, shouting, "Come back! I baked you for tea!"

But the gingerbread man only laughed and ran on, calling, "Run, run, as fast as you can – you won't catch me, I'm the gingerbread man!"

The old woman's husband was digging in the garden and he blinked as he saw the gingerbread man run past. Then he saw his wife running after him and heard her shouting, "Stop

that gingerbread man! He's for our tea!" So the old man dropped his spade and ran after the gingerbread man too.

"Stop!" he shouted. "You're for my tea!"

But the gingerbread man only laughed. "Your wife can't catch me and nor will you! Run, run, as fast as you can – you'll never catch me, I'm the gingerbread man!"

And he ran on down the road, with the old man and the old woman panting after him.

He ran past a cow, and the cow smelled the warm, spicy gingerbread. "Mmm!" said the cow. "Come back, I want to eat you!"

But the gingerbread man only laughed. "The old woman can't catch me, nor the old man. And no cow in the world can! Run, run, as fast as you can – you'll never catch me, I'm the gingerbread man!"

And on he ran. The cow came lumbering after him, and panting along behind the cow came the old man and the old woman, all three of them chasing the runaway gingerbread man.

The gingerbread man ran past a horse, and the horse smelled the spicy gingerbread. "Hey!" said the horse. "Come back! I'd like to eat you!"

But the gingerbread man only laughed. "The old woman can't catch me, nor the old man; the cow can't catch me and no horse in the world can! Run, run, as fast as you can – you'll never catch me, I'm the gingerbread man!"

And on he ran. After him the horse came galloping; and behind the horse the cow came lumbering; and panting along behind the cow came the old man and the old woman – all of them chasing the runaway gingerbread man.

Then the gingerbread man ran past some haymakers who were working in a field. The haymakers smelled the spicy gingerbread and said, "Ooh! Come back, Gingerbread Man! We'd like to eat you!"

But the gingerbread man only laughed and said, "The old woman can't catch me and neither can the old man; the cow can't, the horse can't and no one in the world can! So run, run, as fast as you can – you'll never catch me, I'm the gingerbread man!"

And on he ran. And after him ran all the haymakers, shouting; and behind them came the horse, galloping; and behind the horse, the cow, lumbering; and behind the cow, the old man and the old woman, panting. All of them chasing the runaway gingerbread man.

But ahead of the gingerbread man was a wide, deep river. By the edge of the river sat a fox, watching everything.

The gingerbread man had to stop when he reached the river. He couldn't go into the water or he would melt.

"Now what are you going to do?" asked the fox.

The gingerbread man was afraid of the fox, but he still said, "Run, run, as fast as you can – you'll never catch me, I'm the gingerbread man!"

"I don't want to run," said the fox, "and I don't want to catch you. I never eat gingerbread – it's bad for my teeth. Would you like me to carry you across the river?"

"You won't eat me?" asked the gingerbread man.

"You can sit on my tail, which is farthest from my mouth. I can't eat you then, can I?" said the clever fox.

The gingerbread man thought he would be safe with the fox, so he got onto the fox's tail and the fox started to swim across. The haymakers, the horse, the cow, the old man and the old woman all ran down to the river bank. But it was too late. The gingerbread man waved to them from the fox's tail and shouted, "Run, run, as fast as you can – you'll never catch me, I'm the gingerbread man!"

As the fox swam across the river, his tail got wet, so the gingerbread man climbed a little farther up onto the fox's back.

As the fox swam on, the river got deeper and more and more of his back was under water. The gingerbread man had to move up farther, onto the fox's shoulders. But soon even the fox's shoulders were wet.

"Climb onto my head," said the fox. "You'll be dry there."

So the gingerbread man climbed up onto the fox's head. But soon even the fox's head got splashed. Only his nose was poking above the surface.

"Climb onto my nose," said the fox. "You'll be dry there."

So the gingerbread man climbed onto the fox's nose. But just as the fox reached the other side of the river and was climbing out onto the bank, he gave his nose a quick *flip!*

Up into the air sailed the gingerbread man. The fox opened his mouth wide. Down fell the gingerbread man, right into the fox's mouth – SNAP!

The fox sat on the bank and looked at the haymakers, the horse, the cow, the old man and the old woman on the other side. He licked his lips and said, "Run, run, as fast as you can – it takes a fox to catch a gingerbread man!" Because foxes are clever and they know that it takes more to catch gingerbread men than running after them shouting, "Come back! I want to eat you!"

The Little Red Hen

Once upon a time, in a farmyard, there lived a busy little red hen and her chicks. She was always scratching around, always busy.

A dog, a cat and a pig lived in the farmyard too, but they were lazy. The dog and the cat slept nearly all day, and the pig was always either eating or lying in his mud patch.

One day, the little red hen found a grain of wheat.

"Who will help me plant this grain?" she asked.

"Not I," said the dog.

"Not I," said the cat.

"Not I," said the pig. They were all too idle.

"Then I shall do it, and my chicks will help me," said the little red hen. She scratched a hole in the earth and planted the grain of wheat, and her chicks helped her.

But the earth was dry and the wheat couldn't grow.

"Who will help me water the wheat?" asked the little red hen.

"Not I," said the dog.

"Not I," said the cat.

"Not I," said the pig.

"Then I shall do it, and my chicks will help me," said the little red hen. She carried water from the pump and watered the wheat, and her chicks helped her.

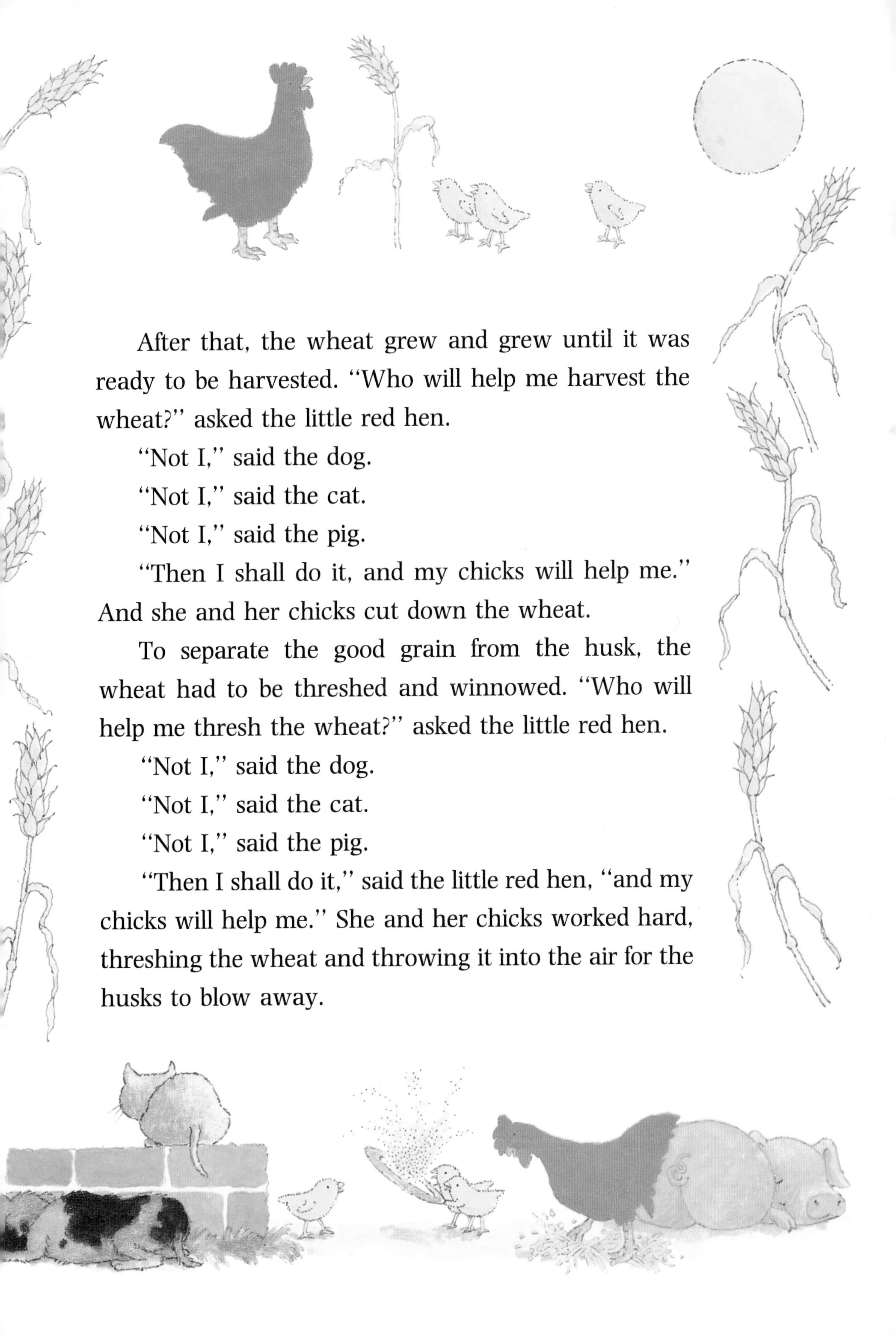

After that, the wheat grew and grew until it was ready to be harvested. "Who will help me harvest the wheat?" asked the little red hen.

"Not I," said the dog.

"Not I," said the cat.

"Not I," said the pig.

"Then I shall do it, and my chicks will help me." And she and her chicks cut down the wheat.

To separate the good grain from the husk, the wheat had to be threshed and winnowed. "Who will help me thresh the wheat?" asked the little red hen.

"Not I," said the dog.

"Not I," said the cat.

"Not I," said the pig.

"Then I shall do it," said the little red hen, "and my chicks will help me." She and her chicks worked hard, threshing the wheat and throwing it into the air for the husks to blow away.

"Who will help me carry the grain to the mill to have it ground into flour?" asked the little red hen.

"Not I," said the dog.

"Not I," said the cat.

"Not I," said the pig.

"Then I shall do it, and my chicks will help me." The little red hen and her chicks carried the grain all the way to the mill. When it was ground, they carried the flour all the way home.

"Now, who will help me bake a cake?" asked the little red hen.

"Not I," said the dog.

"Not I," said the cat.

"Not I," said the pig.

"Then I'll bake it myself," said the little red hen, "and my chicks will help me." She set to work and baked a cake, and her chicks helped her.

When the cake was ready, the little red hen took it out of the oven. A beautiful, sweet, spicy, warm smell drifted over the farmyard. The dog lifted his head and sniffed. The cat twitched her nose and sniffed. The pig sat up in his mud patch and sniffed.

"Who will help me eat this cake?" asked the little red hen.

"I will!" said the dog.

"And I will!" said the cat.

"Me too!" said the pig.

"Oh no, you won't!" said the little red hen. "Not a slice, not a crumb. My chicks and I did all the work, so my chicks and I shall eat all the cake!"

They did, and a fine cake it was. Now all the cake is finished and so is this story.

NURSERY SONGS

Humpty Dumpty *66*
Old King Cole *67*
Little Boy Blue *68*
Ladybird, ladybird *68*
Lavender's blue, dilly, dilly *69*
Old Macdonald had a farm *70*
Three blind mice! *71*
Hickory, dickory, dock *71*
Ding, dong, bell *72*
I love little pussy *72*
Tom, Tom, the piper's son *73*
Georgie Porgie *73*
It's raining, it's pouring *74*
Doctor Foster *74*
One misty, moisty morning *74*
Rain, rain, go away *75*
Rub-a-dub-dub *75*
Sing a song of sixpence *76*
Polly put the kettle on *78*
The muffin man *78*
Pease porridge hot *79*
Jack Sprat could eat no fat *79*
Hot cross buns! *80*
I had a little nut tree *80*
There was a little girl *81*
Peter, Peter, pumpkin eater *81*
Baa, baa, black sheep *82*
Mary, Mary, quite contrary *82*
Christmas is coming *83*
Little Jack Horner *83*
Jingle, bells! *83*
Goosey, goosey gander *84*
Hickety, pickety, my black hen *84*
Pop goes the weasel! *85*
Incey Wincey spider *85*
Yankee Doodle came to town *86*
Bobby Shaftoe's gone to sea *86*
O dear, what can the matter be? *87*
Hey diddle, diddle *88*
Girls and boys, come out to play *89*

Humpty Dumpty sat on a wall,
Humpty Dumpty had a great fall;
All the King's horses,
And all the King's men,
Couldn't put Humpty together again.

Old King Cole was a merry old soul,
And a merry old soul was he;
He called for his pipe,
And he called for his bowl,
And he called for his fiddlers three.

Every fiddler he had a fiddle,
And a very fine fiddle had he;
Oh, there's none so rare
As can compare
With King Cole and his fiddlers three.

Little Boy Blue,
Come blow your horn.
The sheep's in the meadow,
The cow's in the corn.
Where is the boy
Who looks after the sheep?
He's under a haystack
Fast asleep.
Will you wake him?
No, not I,
For if I do,
He's sure to cry.

Ladybird, ladybird,
Fly away home,
Your house is on fire
Your children all gone;
All but one,
And her name is Ann,
And she has crept under
The warming pan.

Lavender's blue, dilly, dilly,
Lavender's green;
When I am king, dilly, dilly,
You shall be queen.

Call up your men, dilly, dilly,
Set them to work,
Some to the plough, dilly, dilly,
Some to the cart.

Some to make hay, dilly, dilly,
Some to thresh corn,
Whilst you and I, dilly, dilly,
Keep ourselves warm.

Old Macdonald had a farm,
E-I-E-I-O.
And on that farm he had
some cows,
E-I-E-I-O.
With a moo-moo here,
And a moo-moo there,
Here a moo, there a moo,
Everywhere a moo-moo,
Old Macdonald had a farm,
E-I-E-I-O.

Old Macdonald had a farm,
E-I-E-I-O.
And on that farm he had some
pigs . . . sheep . . . horses . . .
cats . . . dogs . . . ducks.

☆ *Repeat the song with different animals and noises.*

Three blind mice! Three blind mice!
See how they run! See how they run!
They all ran after the farmer's wife,
Who cut off their tails with a carving knife;
Did you ever see such a thing in your life,
As three blind mice?

Hickory, dickory, dock,
The mouse ran up the clock.
The clock struck one,
The mouse ran down,
Hickory, dickory, dock.

Ding, dong, bell,
Pussy's in the well.
Who put her in?
 Little Johnny Green.
Who pulled her out?
 Little Tommy Stout.
What a naughty boy was that
To try to drown poor pussy cat,
Who never did him any harm,
But killed the mice in his
 father's barn.

I love little pussy,
 Her coat is so warm,
And if I don't hurt her
 She'll do me no harm.

So I'll not pull her tail,
 Nor drive her away,
But pussy and I
 Very gently will play.

She shall sit by my side,
 And I'll give her some food;
And pussy will love me
 Because I am good.

Tom, Tom, the piper's son,
Stole a pig and away did run;
The pig was eat,
And Tom was beat,
And Tom went howling
Down the street.

Georgie Porgie,
pudding and pie,
Kissed the girls
and made them cry.
When the boys
came out to play,
Georgie Porgie
ran away.

It's raining, it's pouring,
The old man's snoring;
He got into bed
And bumped his head
And couldn't get up in
the morning.

Doctor Foster went to Gloucester
In a shower of rain;
He stepped in a puddle,
Right up to his middle,
And never went there again.

One misty, moisty morning,
When cloudy was the weather,
I met a little old man
Clothed all in leather.

He began to compliment,
And I began to grin,
How do you do, and how do you do,
And how do you do again?

Rain, rain, go away,
Come again another day,
All the children want to play.
Rain, rain, go to Spain,
Never show your face again.

Rub-a-dub-dub,
Three men in a tub,
And who do you think they be?
The butcher, the baker,
The candlestick-maker;
Turn 'em out, knaves all three!

Sing a song of sixpence,
A pocket full of rye;
Four-and-twenty blackbirds,
Baked in a pie.

When the pie was opened,
The birds began to sing;
Was not that a dainty dish,
To set before the king?

The king was in his counting-house,
Counting out his money;
The queen was in the parlour
Eating bread and honey.

The maid was in the garden,
Hanging out the clothes,
When down came a blackbird
And pecked off her nose.

☆ *Happy ending:*
Along came Jenny Wren
And stuck her nose back on again.

Polly put the kettle on,
Polly put the kettle on,
Polly put the kettle on,
We'll all have tea.

Sukey take it off again,
Sukey take it off again,
Sukey take it off again,
They've all gone away.

Oh, do you know the muffin man,
The muffin man, the muffin man,
Oh, do you know the muffin man
Who lives in Drury Lane?

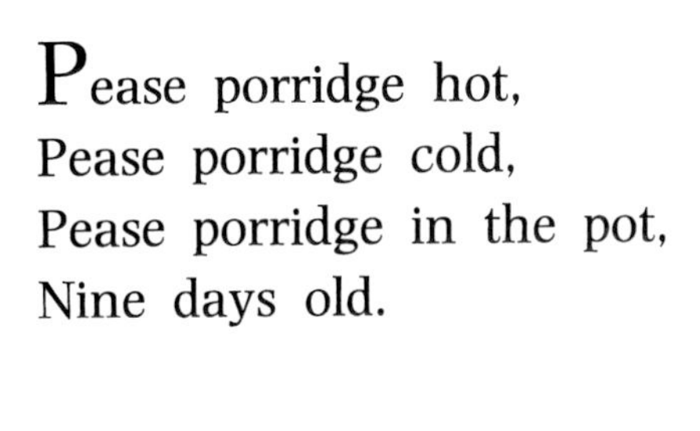

Pease porridge hot,
Pease porridge cold,
Pease porridge in the pot,
Nine days old.

Some like it hot,
Some like it cold,
Some like it in the pot,
Nine days old.

Jack Sprat could eat no fat,
His wife could eat no lean,
And so between them both, you see,
They licked the platter clean.

Hot cross buns! Hot cross buns!
One a penny, two a penny,
hot cross buns.
If you have no daughters,
Give them to your sons.
One a penny, two a penny,
hot cross buns.

I had a little nut tree,
Nothing would it bear
But a silver nutmeg
And a golden pear;
The king of Spain's daughter
Came to visit me,
And all for the sake
Of my little nut tree.

There was a little girl,
And she had a little curl
Right in the middle of her forehead;
When she was good,
She was very, very good,
But when she was bad,
She was horrid.

Peter, Peter, pumpkin eater,
Had a wife and couldn't
keep her;
He put her in a pumpkin shell,
And there he kept her
very well.

Baa, baa, black sheep,
  Have you any wool?
Yes, sir, yes, sir,
  Three bags full;

One for the master,
  And one for the dame,
And one for the little boy
  Who lives down the lane.

Mary, Mary, quite contrary,
  How does your garden grow?
With silver bells and cockle shells,
  And pretty maids all in a row.

Christmas is coming,
The geese are getting fat,
Please to put a penny
In the old man's hat.
If you haven't got a penny,
A ha'penny will do;
If you haven't got a ha'penny,
Then God bless you!

Little Jack Horner
Sat in the corner,
Eating his Christmas pie;
He put in his thumb,
And pulled out a plum,
And said: What a good boy am I!

Jingle, bells! Jingle, bells!
Jingle all the way;
Oh, what fun it is to ride
In a one-horse open sleigh.

Goosey, goosey gander,
Whither shall I wander?
Upstairs and downstairs
And in my lady's chamber.
There I met an old man
Who would not say his prayers,
I took him by the left leg
And threw him down the stairs.

Hickety, pickety, my black hen,
She lays eggs for gentlemen;
Sometimes one, and sometimes ten,
Hickety, pickety, my black hen.

Up and down the City Road,
In and out the Eagle,
That's the way the money goes,
Pop goes the weasel!

Half a pound of tuppenny rice,
Half a pound of treacle,
Mix it up and make it nice,
Pop goes the weasel!

Incey Wincey spider,
Climbing up the spout;
Down came the rain
And washed the spider out.

Out came the sunshine
And dried up all the rain;
Incey Wincey spider,
Climbing up again.

Yankee Doodle came to town,
Riding on a pony;
He stuck a feather in his cap
And called it macaroni.

First he bought a porridge pot,
And then he bought a ladle,
And then he trotted home again
As fast as he was able.

Bobby Shaftoe's gone to sea,
Silver buckles on his knee;
He'll come back and marry me,
Bonny Bobby Shaftoe.

Bobby Shaftoe's bright and fair,
Combing down his yellow hair;
He's my love for evermore,
Bonny Bobby Shaftoe.

O dear, what can the matter be?
Dear, dear, what can the matter be?
O dear, what can the matter be?
Johnny's so long at the fair.

He promised he'd buy me a fairing should please me,
And then for a kiss, oh! he vowed he would tease me,
He promised he'd bring me a bunch of blue ribbons
To tie up my bonny brown hair.

And it's O dear, what can the matter be?
Dear, dear, what can the matter be?
O dear, what can the matter be?
Johnny's so long at the fair.

He promised he'd bring me a basket of posies,
A garland of lilies, a garland of roses,
A little straw hat, to set off the blue ribbons
That tie up my bonny brown hair.

Hey diddle, diddle,
The cat and the fiddle,
The cow jumped over the moon;
The little dog laughed
To see such sport,
And the dish ran away with the spoon.

Girls and boys, come out to play,
The moon doth shine as bright as day.
Leave your supper and leave your sleep,
And come with your playfellows into the street.
Come with a whoop and come with a call,
Come with a good will or not at all.
Up the ladder and down the wall,
A half-penny loaf will serve us all;
You find milk, and I'll find flour,
And we'll have a pudding in half an hour.

ANIMAL TALES

The Three Billy Goats Gruff
92

The Lion and the Mouse
98

The House on the Hill
99

Brer Rabbit and the Tar Baby
103

The Town Mouse and
the Country Mouse
108

The Hare and the Tortoise
115

The Three Billy Goats Gruff

Once upon a time there were three billy goats – Little Billy Goat Gruff, Middle-Sized Billy Goat Gruff and Great Big Billy Goat Gruff. They'd been shut in a shed all winter with nothing to eat but hay and they were very thin. But now it was spring, and they set off for the mountain meadows to eat the sweet, new, juicy, spring grass.

"You two go ahead," said Great Big Billy Goat Gruff. "There's a thistle or two here I mean to eat before I go on." So Middle-Sized Billy Goat Gruff and Little Billy Goat Gruff went on without him.

Then, "You go on ahead," said Middle-Sized Billy Goat Gruff to Little Billy Goat Gruff. "There are just one or two leaves on this thorn-bush I mean to eat before I go on." So Little Billy Goat Gruff went on alone.

To reach the mountain meadow where the sweet, new, juicy, spring grass grew, Little Billy Goat Gruff had to cross a

wooden bridge over a high waterfall. Under the bridge lived a troll – a horrible, howling, gobbling, greedy troll with a nose as long as a kitchen spoon. As Little Billy Goat Gruff crossed the bridge, his hooves went trip-trip-trip on the wooden planks. The troll underneath heard him and yelled out, "Who's that trip-tripping across *my* bridge?"

"It's only me," said Little Billy Goat Gruff. "I'm just going to get fat on the sweet, new, juicy, spring grass over there in the meadow."

The troll was furious. He jumped up onto the bridge in front of Little Billy Goat Gruff. "Nobody crosses *my* bridge!" he yelled. "I'm going to eat you, little goat. I'm going to eat you from your horns to your heels."

"Oh, please don't eat me! You wouldn't enjoy me!" said Little Billy Goat Gruff. "I'm so small and skinny, I'd hardly be a mouthful. Why don't you wait for my brother, Middle-Sized Billy Goat Gruff? He'd make a much better meal."

The troll thought about it. "You *are* skinny," he said. "Hardly worth chewing. Yes, get off my bridge! I'll wait for your brother."

Little Billy Goat Gruff ran quickly across the bridge, trip-trip-trip, and was soon among the sweet, new, juicy, spring grass on the other side, eating as much as he could.

The troll went back under the bridge and waited.

Soon Middle-Sized Billy Goat Gruff had finished the leaves on the thorn-bush and came across the bridge. His middle-sized hooves went trot-trot-trot on the wooden planks. The troll underneath heard him and yelled out, "Who's that trot-trotting across *my* bridge?"

"Only me," said Middle-Sized Billy Goat Gruff. "I'm going to the meadow to eat the sweet, new, juicy, spring grass."

Up onto the bridge jumped the troll. He was furious. "Nobody crosses *my* bridge," he screamed. "I'm going to eat you, every scrap of you, from your horns to your heels. That'll teach you to trot-trot-trot your nasty hooves across *my* bridge."

"You don't want to eat me," said Middle-Sized Billy Goat Gruff. "I'm not nearly big enough to fill your belly."

"You're bigger than your skinny little brother," said the greedy troll.

"Yes," said Middle-Sized Billy Goat Gruff, "but I'm not nearly as big as our brother, Great Big Billy Goat Gruff. He's twice as big as I am. He would make a meal fit for a troll."

The troll thought about it. "You're right," he said. "It makes sense to wait for the biggest of you. Get off my bridge then, before I eat you anyway!"

Middle-Sized Billy Goat Gruff ran quickly across the bridge and reached the meadow where Little Billy Goat Gruff was eating the sweet, new, juicy, spring grass.

The troll went back under the bridge and waited.

Soon Great Big Billy Goat Gruff had finished his thistles, so he started across the wooden bridge to join his brothers. Tramp, tramp, tramp went his great big hooves on the wooden planks. Underneath, the troll was listening and he roared, "Who's that tramp-tramping across *my* bridge?"

"I am," said Great Big Billy Goat Gruff. "I'm going to join my brothers in the meadow and we're all going to get fat."

The troll was furious to hear that. He jumped up onto the bridge and landed in front of Great Big Billy Goat Gruff. "Nobody crosses *my* bridge!" said the troll.

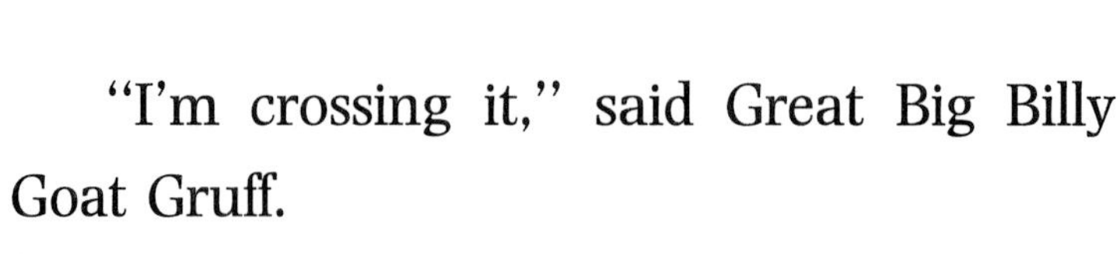

"I'm crossing it," said Great Big Billy Goat Gruff.

"No you're not!" screamed the troll. "I'm going to eat you up, horns, hair and heels! You're going to fill my belly until it feels as if I've eaten half the world. I'm going to . . ."

"Come and try!" said Great Big Billy Goat Gruff. He lowered his big-horned head and said:

"On my head are two sharp spears;
With them I'll make you cry salt tears!
On my head are two big stones;
I'll thump you hard and smash
your bones!"

Then he charged at the troll and speared him, thumped him and tossed him right over the sun and moon.

High in the air soared the troll, then down, down, down he fell. But he didn't land on the bridge. He missed the bridge altogether and fell even farther – down, down, down the waterfall until SPLASH! that was the end of the troll.

Then Great Big Billy Goat Gruff went tramp, tramp, tramp across the bridge and joined his brothers in the meadow on the other side. They all got fat eating the sweet, new, juicy, spring grass. For all I know they're still there, growing fatter and fatter every day.

And that's all I know of them because – Snip, Snap, Snout, this tale's told out.

The Lion and the Mouse

A lion was once sleeping in the sun when a mouse ran over his paw and woke him. The lion reached out his paw and caught the mouse by the tail.

"Oh, don't kill me, please! Let me go and I'll do you a good turn one day," squeaked the mouse.

"You're too small ever to be able to do me a good turn," said the lion. "But I'll let you go because you're too small to be worth eating."

Now that very night the lion walked into a trap set by hunters. A net made of strong rope fell over him and he couldn't move. Soon the hunters would come and kill him.

But then he heard a squeak and saw the mouse he had allowed to go free. With sharp little teeth she began to bite through the ropes. At last all the ropes were chewed right through and the lion was free.

"I was wrong," said the lion. "I thought you were too small to be of any use to anyone, little mouse, but you have saved my life."

After that the lion remembered that the small and weak can still be of help, even to the strongest.

The House on the Hill

Once upon a time a pig with a curly tail grew tired of living in his sty.

"I think," he said to his friend the sheep, "I shall build myself a house."

"Good idea," said the sheep.

"On a hill," said the pig.

"Oooh," said the sheep. "Can I come too?"

"Well," said the pig, "what can you do to help?"

Sheep thought hard for a moment.

"I can pull the logs to build the walls," he said.

"Come on then," said the pig.

So the two of them, Pig and Sheep, set off together and on the road they met a goose.

"Good morning, Pig," said the goose. "Good morning, Sheep. Where are you two going?"

"We're going to build a house," said Pig.

"On a hill," said Sheep.

"Oooh," said Goose. "Can I come too?"

"Well," said Pig, "what can you do to help?"

Goose put her head on one side to think.

"I can collect moss with my sharp beak," she said, "and I can stuff it into the cracks of the logs. That will keep out the wind and the rain."

"Come on then," said Pig.

So the three of them, Pig, Sheep and Goose, set off together. On the way they met a rabbit.

"Good morning, Pig," said the rabbit. "And good morning, Sheep and Goose. Where are you three going?"

"We're going to build a house," said Pig.

"On a hill," said Sheep.

"With logs and moss," said Goose.

"Oooh," said the rabbit. "Can I come too?"

"Well," said Pig, "what can you do to help?"

Rabbit stopped to think for a moment. Then he said, "I could dig the holes for the logs."

"Come on then," said Pig.

So the four of them, Pig, Sheep, Goose and Rabbit, set off together and on the way they met a cockerel.

"Good morning, Pig, Sheep, Goose and Rabbit," he said. "Where are you four going?"

"We're going to build a house," said Pig.

"On a hill," said Sheep.

"With logs for walls," said Goose, "and moss to keep the wind out."

"And holes to keep the logs in place," said Rabbit.

"Oooh," said the cockerel. "Can I come too?"

"Well," said Pig, "what can you do to help?"

Cockerel thought. "I know," he said, "I can crow very early each morning and wake you up to begin your work."

"Come on then," said Pig.

So the five of them, Pig, Sheep, Goose, Rabbit and Cockerel, set off together. And soon they came to a hill.

"This is where I shall build my house," said Pig. And they all set to work.

Pig sniffed out the logs with his big snout; Sheep pulled them up the hill with his strong legs; Goose dug up moss with her sharp beak and stuffed it into the cracks; and Rabbit dug holes for the posts.

And every morning, very early, Cock crowed to wake them all up so they could begin their work.

The house grew and grew. Soon it was finished and all the animals sat back and looked up at the house they had built on the hill.

Then Cock flew up onto the roof and crowed and crowed with delight.

"Cock a doodle do!
Just come and look, please do!
We've worked away with such a will,
To build this house upon the hill.
Don't you think we've built it well?
And now inside we mean to dwell!"

Then everyone who lived for miles around heard the cock's song and knew that the house on the hill was finished.

And when they looked towards the house, they saw lights in the windows and smoke rising from the chimney and they knew that inside the house the five friends were sitting together in great happiness.

Brer Rabbit and the Tar Baby

Foxes like eating rabbits, and Brer Fox had been trying for a long time to catch Brer Rabbit and eat him. But Brer Rabbit always managed to get away somehow, by one trick or another. It made Brer Fox mad.

Now Brer Fox was walking along the road one day and he came across some tar that had been left there. It was a hot day and the tar was soft and sticky in the sun. Brer Fox thought of a way he could use that sticky tar to catch Brer Rabbit.

Brer Fox got some twigs and covered them with sticky tar until he had made a sort of baby-shape. He stood it up by the side of the road and then he went and hid himself in a bush.

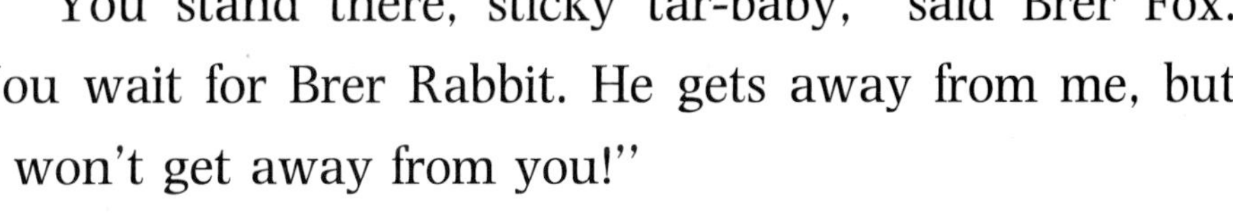

"You stand there, sticky tar-baby," said Brer Fox. "You wait for Brer Rabbit. He gets away from me, but he won't get away from you!"

After a while, along came Brer Rabbit, hopping and jumping with his tail stuck up behind him.

Brer Rabbit saw the tar-baby standing by the side of the road and he called out, "Good morning to you!"

The tar-baby said nothing.

Well, Brer Rabbit thought the tar-baby hadn't heard him, so he went a bit closer and he spoke a bit louder. "Good morning!" he said. "It's a fine day."

The tar-baby said nothing.

"Are you deaf?" shouted Brer Rabbit. "I said 'Good morning' to you twice and you just stand there saying nothing. Some folk would think that very rude."

The tar-baby said nothing.

"Well, you sure are high and mighty," said Brer Rabbit. "When someone says 'Good morning' to you, it's polite to say 'Good morning' back. Let's hear you say it."

But the tar-baby said nothing.

Brer Rabbit was angry. "If you don't say 'Good morning', I'm going to let you have one right on the chin!"

The tar-baby still said nothing.

So Brer Rabbit punched the tar-baby right on the chin. But the tar-baby was sticky and Brer Rabbit's paw stuck to the tar. No matter how hard Brer Rabbit pulled, he couldn't get his paw free.

"Let me go!" Brer Rabbit shouted, while Brer Fox laughed to himself in the bush nearby. "Let me go or I'll hit you with the other paw!"

But the tar-baby said nothing and it didn't let Brer Rabbit go.

So Brer Rabbit hit the tar-baby as hard as he could with the other paw. And his other paw got stuck too. Now Brer Rabbit had both front paws stuck to the tar-baby and he couldn't get loose, no matter how he struggled. "Let me go," said Brer Rabbit, "or I'll kick you!"

But the tar-baby didn't let him go.

So Brer Rabbit kicked the tar-baby and got his foot stuck in the sticky tar and couldn't get it loose. Then Brer Rabbit kicked the tar-baby with the other foot and that got stuck too. So there was Brer Rabbit with all four feet stuck in the tar, and he couldn't get loose, no matter how he struggled and how he yelled.

Then Brer Fox came out of his bush, laughing.

"You think you're so clever," said Brer Fox, "but you're just a plain fool. I'm going to eat you, Brer Rabbit, and that'll be the end of you!"

"Oh," said Brer Rabbit, "cook me and eat me and I hope you enjoy me. That's not half as bad as what I thought you were going to do."

Brer Fox was puzzled.

"What did you think I was going to do?" he asked.

"Oh, I thought you were going to throw me in the briar patch," replied Brer Rabbit.

"Throwing you in the briar patch is worse than cooking and eating you?"

"Oh yes!"

"Well then, I'll hang you from a tree," said Brer Fox. "That'll be worse than eating you and worse then throwing you in the briar patch."

"Hang me from a tree, cook me and eat me," said Brer Rabbit, "only please, please don't throw me in that terrible briar patch!"

"Then I *will* throw you in the briar patch!" said Brer Fox, and he tore Brer Rabbit off the tar-baby and threw him right into the middle of the briar patch.

"There!" laughed Brer Fox. "Now I've had my own back for all those times you tricked me and laughed at me! Serves you right, Brer Rabbit!"

But not a sound came from Brer Rabbit in the briar patch. Brer Fox stopped laughing and listened. Then he heard singing – Brer Rabbit *singing* in the briar patch.

This is the song:

"I was born and bred in a briar patch, Brer Fox!
Thorns'll never hurt me, Brer Fox!
I've lived all my life in a briar patch, Brer Fox!
I'm right where I want to be, Brer Fox!"

So Brer Rabbit tricked Brer Fox and got away, again! Brer Fox sneaked off and didn't dare show his face for a good many days. All the rabbits would have laughed at him if he had.

And that's the end of the story – but it was a good one while it lasted.

The Town Mouse and the Country Mouse

Once upon a time there lived a mouse – a smart sort of fellow – whose home was in a very grand house in a town. Every day he ate the best food and sipped the best wines, while at night he slept in a warm little hole in the corner of the kitchen floor.

One day, however, he thought he'd like a change. "I could do with a holiday," he thought to himself. "I think I'll go and see my cousin, the country mouse, and get a breath of country air."

So he packed his bag, checked that his hole was clean and tidy to come back to and off he went.

His cousin was delighted to see him.

"Come in, come in," he said. "Make yourself at home. I'll prepare a special meal for you."

And presently he invited his cousin to come to the table, where he had laid a cloth with two plates of bread and cheese, a few tomatoes and a small leaf of lettuce.

The town mouse nibbled a little cheese. He took a mouthful or two of tomato and bread; he sipped at his clear cool water. All the time he was thinking rather longingly of the meal he might be enjoying at his own home – a lamb chop perhaps, a portion of apple pie and cream, all washed down with a glass of wine. But he quickly put such thoughts aside as being ungrateful. He knew the country mouse was giving him the best food he could find.

"And now," said the country mouse, "you must be tired after your journey. Let me show you my guest hole."

And he led him to a small scooped out hole in the bank of a cornfield. Once again the town mouse thought of his own warm nest, of the delicious smells of food that tickled his nose all night long and gave him such pleasant dreams. But he

knew his cousin was giving him the best care he could, so he thanked him politely and settled down for the night.

But he could not sleep.

At first it was too quiet. There were no sounds of traffic outside the door; there were no bursts of conversation from other rooms; there were no footsteps, no distant music such as he could always hear in his own home, where the sounds drifted down from the rooms upstairs.

He turned and tossed and tossed and turned.

Then he began to hear noises. He heard little scrabblings and scratchings as small night creatures came out of their homes and went about their business in the surrounding fields. And then – he shivered with fear at the sound – he heard the great whooping cry of an owl, "Too-wit! Too-woo!"

And it seemed as if he had no sooner closed his eyes when, "Breakfast!" called his cousin. "Time to get up!" And there on the breakfast table were a few grains of corn and barley, a glass of water and . . . nothing else.

Enough was enough, thought the town mouse. It was time to go

home. But what could he tell his cousin, who had been so welcoming? At last he thought of what to say.

"Dear cousin," he said, "you have made me so welcome that I should like you to come back and stay with me for a few days. It is very quiet here and I think perhaps you would like to see a little of town life?"

"Delighted," said the country mouse. They set off together that very night and by dawn were safely inside the town house kitchen.

"Aha!" said the town mouse, rubbing his paws together with delight. "I see there was a party here last night! We have some roast beef, some special ice cream, a few cheeses . . . come and help yourself."

The country mouse squeaked in amazement at the sight of all that rich food.

But just as they had begun their feast, CRASH! BANG! the kitchen door burst open and in came the cook in a great hurry. "Now where's the bacon?" she muttered to herself. "Where are those eggs?" And she rattled and clattered among the shelves of the larder until the country mouse, who was crouched behind a great pitcher of milk, thought he would die of fright.

When the cook had gone, the town mouse – not at all worried – popped out from behind a very large ham, saying cheerfully, "All safe now! Come on out, my dear!"

But every time they began to eat, the same thing happened. CRASH! BANG! would go the door and in would come someone looking for food, or plates, or a frying pan. There was never a moment's peace.

By night-time the poor country mouse was shaking like a jelly.

"Oh, it gets worse at night," the town mouse assured him. "That's when we have really big feasts in this house. And the food they leave! You won't believe your eyes."

"I d . . . d . . . don't think I'll be here to see it!" said the country mouse. "I know my food is plain and simple; I know the country life is too quiet for an educated chap like you, but it suits me. And even though the food here is delicious, I never get the chance to eat it!" And a great tear rolled sadly down one cheek.

"Oh please," said the town mouse, "don't be upset! I know how it is. Your life suits you but it doesn't suit me. This life suits me but it doesn't suit you – now where's the harm in that? We are both happy where we are and, after all, we can always visit each other from time to time, can't we? It's so much better to live in the way each of us finds most comfortable."

"Ye . . . es," agreed the country mouse. "Can I go now?"

So the town mouse packed a small hamper for his cousin. In it he put a portion of salmon, a slice of pork pie, a little pâté and a few strawberries.

"There," he said. "You'll be back home for breakfast! Goodbye, Cousin, we'll see each other again soon."

And back he went to his kitchen and his rich food, where he never noticed all the comings and goings because he had grown so used to them.

And, scurrying along by the hedgerows, crossing fields, the country mouse was making his way back to his quiet little home. Around him he could hear the scrabblings and scratchings of small night creatures looking for food. He heard the great whooping cry of the owl, "Too-wit! Too-woo!" But these were the noises he was used to and they didn't worry him at all.

And at last he came to his own home in the scooped-out bank of the cornfield and, with a sigh of satisfaction, he said to himself, "It's best to stay in the place that suits you best."

So he unpacked his hamper, and in the peace of the early morning he ate a hearty breakfast of salmon and strawberries. "The pork pie and pâté I'll save for supper," he said to himself. And then, feeling very drowsy after his journey and his large breakfast, he curled himself up into a ball and fell fast asleep. With not a sound to disturb him.

The Hare and the Tortoise

Once upon a time a hare sat looking at a tortoise who was chewing a lettuce leaf.

"You eat slowly," he said, "and you walk slowly. Don't you get tired of always being so slow?"

"Nope," said the tortoise.

"Now I'm very fast," continued the hare. "I can run like the wind. I could run all round this field and back again before you've finished chewing that leaf. Shall I try?"

"Yep," said the tortoise.

Off set the hare . . . *whee* . . . *whizz* . . . down the field, round the corners . . . *puff, pant, pant, puff* . . . and he screeched to a halt just as the last mouthful of leaf was disappearing down the tortoise's throat.

"See what I mean?" he asked.

"Yep," said the tortoise.

"Let's have a race," said the hare. "Of course I'll win, but let's see how fast I can run. We'll go right round the field and back here. Are you ready?"

"Yep," said the tortoise.

"Ready . . . steady . . . go!" shouted the hare. And off they went.

The hare raced. The tortoise plodded. *Whee . . . whizz . . .* the hare looked behind him. The tortoise wasn't even in sight.

"Hmm," thought Hare. "I'll just have a snack of those fine-looking leaves over there. Plenty of time. Old Plod will never catch me up."

The leaves were delicious. The hare ate and ate. He ate so much his tummy looked like a balloon.

"Whew!" he said. He looked round. The tortoise was *just* in sight . . . plod, plod, plod.

So off he raced. Heels in the air, ears flattened. *Whee . . . whizz . . .* screeching round the corner. Then he stopped and looked behind. No sign of Old Plod.

"I'm nearly home now," thought Hare. "I've plenty of time for a rest – and I do feel rather full!" He lay down in the shade of some bushes and was soon fast asleep.

When at last he woke up, he stretched himself and yawned.

"I suppose I'd better finish this race," he thought. "Though there's no need to hurry – I'm nearly home."

So he got to his feet and began to saunter the last few yards. But as he turned the last corner, what did he see? Tortoise chewing a lettuce leaf.

"Wh . . . what's happened?" he stammered. "H . . . how did you get here? Did you really go all round the field?"

"Yep," said the tortoise.

"But . . . but . . . I looked back when I was having a snack . . . you weren't anywhere near."

"Nope."

"And when I woke up from my nap you were nowhere to be seen!"

"Nope."

"Then how did you get here first?" asked Hare.

"Just kept plodding," said Plod. "Didn't stop for a snack or a sleep. Just plodded." And with that he finished the last mouthful of lettuce leaf and walked slowly off.

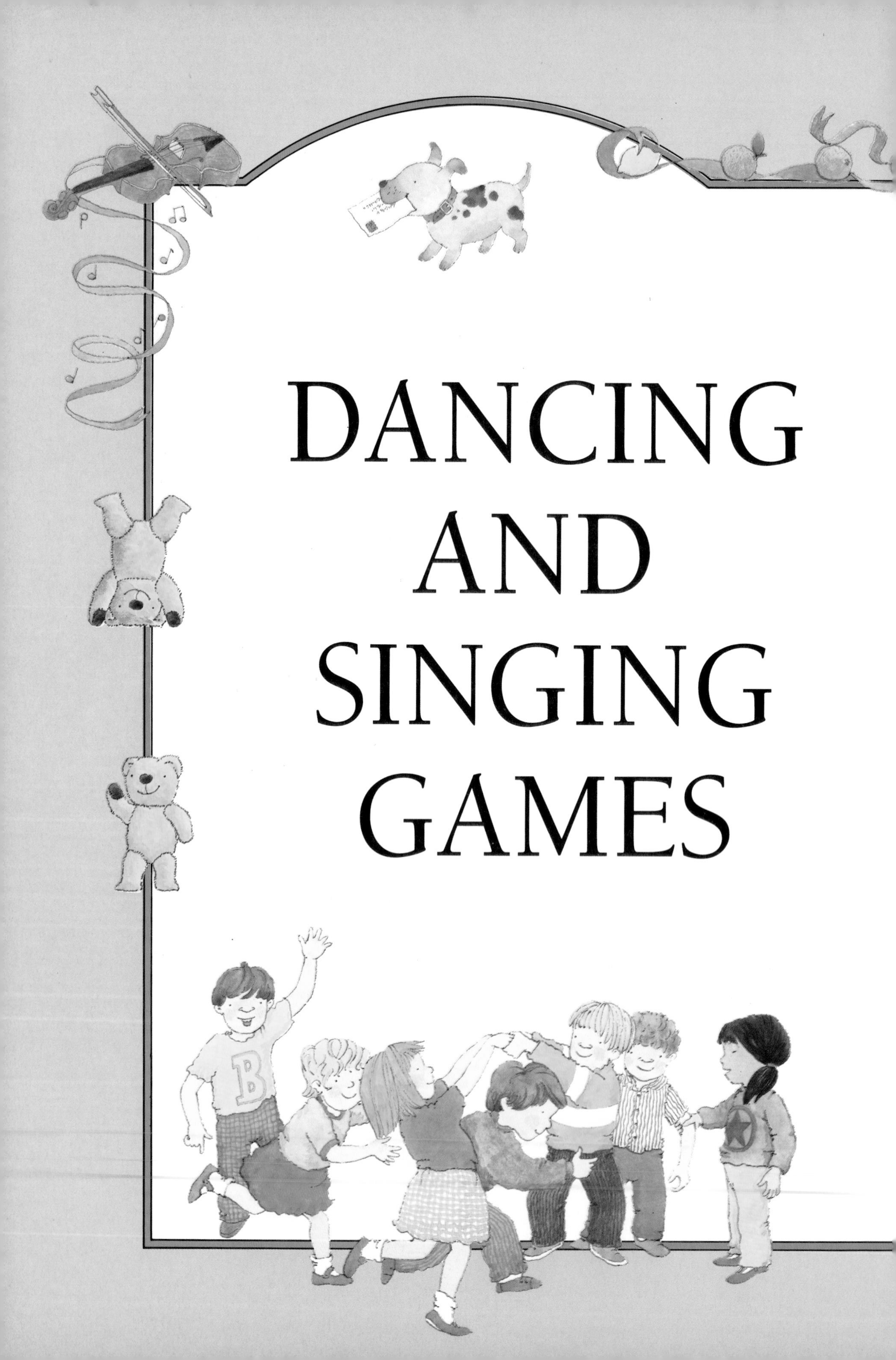

DANCING AND SINGING GAMES

Head and shoulders *120*
If you're happy and you know it *120*
Teddybear, teddybear *121*
Oh, the grand old Duke of York *122*
Can you walk on tiptoe? *123*
Jack be nimble *124*
Little Jumping Joan *124*
Handy Pandy *124*
American jump! *125*
Round and round the rugged rock *126*
Stepping over stepping stones *126*
Here we go round the mulberry bush *127*
Miss Polly had a dolly *128*
One day I went to sea *128*
Oh, we can play on the big bass drum *129*
See-saw, Margery Daw *130*
Sally go round the sun *130*
Swing me low *130*
What's your name? *131*
The wood was dark *131*
Oranges and lemons *132*
London Bridge is falling down *133*
I'm a little teapot *134*
I can tie my shoelaces *134*
The Farmer's in the den *135*
Frère Jacques *136*
I hear thunder *137*
The wheels on the bus *138*
Here we go looby-loo *140*
Three times round *141*
I sent a letter to my love *141*

Head and shoulders, knees and toes,
knees and toes,
Head and shoulders, knees and toes,
knees and toes,

☆ *Touch each part of the body as you sing.*

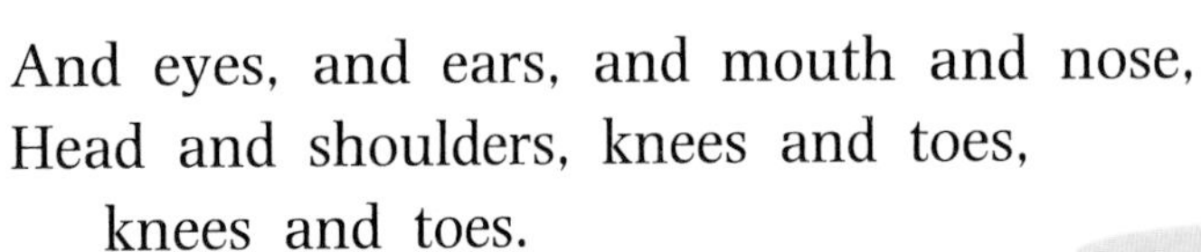

And eyes, and ears, and mouth and nose,
Head and shoulders, knees and toes,
knees and toes.

If you're happy and you know it,
clap your hands,
If you're happy and you know it,
clap your hands,
If you're happy and you know it,
and you really want to show it,
If you're happy and you know it,
clap your hands.

If you're happy and you know it,
stamp your feet . . .
If you're happy and you know it,
nod your head . . .
If you're happy and you know it,
shout "Hooray!" . . .

☆ *Copy the actions.*

☆ *Copy the actions.*

Teddybear, teddybear,
dance on your toes.

Teddybear, teddybear,
touch your nose.

Teddybear, teddybear,
stand on your head.

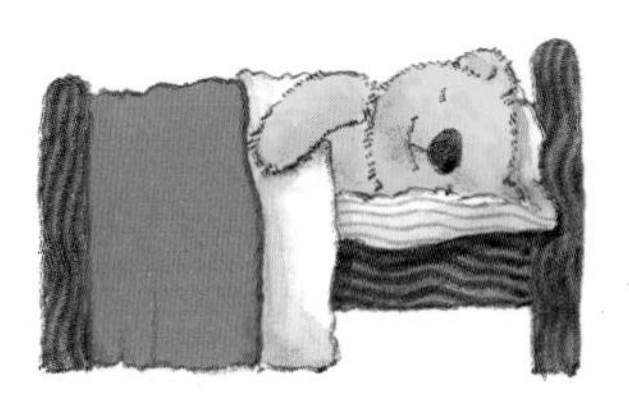

Teddybear, teddybear,
go to bed.

Teddybear, teddybear,
wake up now.

Teddybear, teddybear,
make your bow.

Teddybear, teddybear,
touch the ground.

Teddybear, teddybear,
turn right around.

Teddybear, teddybear,
run upstairs.

Teddybear, teddybear,
say your prayers.

Teddybear, teddybear,
turn off the light.

Teddybear, teddybear,
say goodnight.

Oh, the grand old Duke of York,
He had ten thousand men.
He marched them up
to the top of the hill
And he marched them down again.

And when they were up,
they were up,
And when they were down,
they were down,
And when they were only
half-way up,
They were neither up nor down.

☆ *Sit the baby or toddler on your lap and walk his legs or jog in time to the song. Swing him UP and DOWN at those words. Older children will enjoy marching in time, jumping UP and crouching DOWN.*

Can you walk on tiptoe
As softly as a cat?

Can you stamp along the road
STAMP, STAMP, just like that?

Can you take some great big strides
Just like a giant can?

Or walk along so slowly,
Like a bent old man?

Jack be nimble,
Jack be quick,
Jack JUMP over
the candlestick.

☆ *With a baby, try crossing your legs and sitting him on the top ankle facing you. Hold his hands and swing him up and down. At JUMP swing him into the air and onto your knee.*

Here am I,
Little Jumping Joan;
When nobody's with me
I'm all alone.

Handy Pandy, Jack-a-dandy,
Loves plum cake and sugar candy,
He bought some at the
grocer's shop,
And out he came, hop, hop, hop!

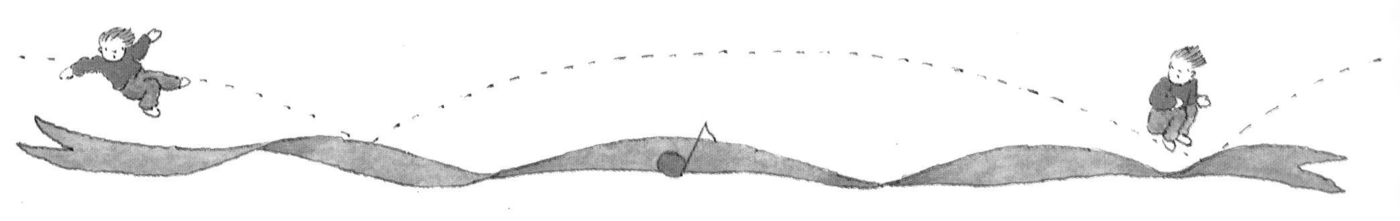

American jump! American jump!
One – Two – Three!
Under the water catching fishes,
Catching fishes for my tea.
Dead . . .
Or alive . . .
Or around the world?

☆ *Holding the child under her arms or by the hands, jump her up three times. Catch her around your waist at THREE, then lower her backwards to catch a fish, and offer a choice of "Dead or alive or around the world".*
For DEAD, lower her to the ground.
For ALIVE, swing her up high.
For AROUND THE WORLD, swing her over your back and down again.

Round and round the rugged rock
The ragged rascal ran.
How many R's are there in that?
Now tell me if you can.

Stepping over stepping stones,
One, two, three,
Stepping over stepping stones,
Come with me.
The river's very fast,
And the river's very wide,
And we'll step across on
    stepping stones
And reach the other side.

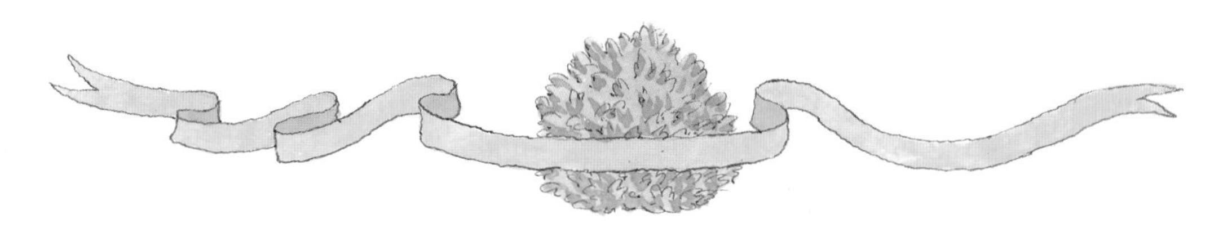

Here we go round the mulberry bush,
The mulberry bush, the mulberry bush,
Here we go round the mulberry bush,
On a cold and frosty morning.

☆ Join hands and dance in a circle. Stop to do the actions of the next verses, repeating the first verse and its dance after each one.

This is the way we wash our hands,
Wash our hands, wash our hands,
This is the way we wash our hands,
On a cold and frosty morning.

This is the way we wash our face . . .
This is the way we brush our hair . . .
This is the way we clean our teeth . . .
This is way we put on our clothes . . .

☆ *A hand-clapping rhyme.*

Miss Polly had a dolly
who was sick, sick, sick,
So she phoned for the doctor
to be quick, quick, quick.
The doctor came
with her bag and her hat,
And she knocked on the door
with a rat-a-tat-tat.

She looked at the dolly
and she shook her head,
And she said, "Miss Polly,
put her straight to bed."
She wrote on a paper
for a pill, pill, pill,
"I'll be back in the morning
with my bill, bill, bill."

One day I went to sea,
chop, knee,
To see what I could see,
chop, knee,
But all that I could see,
chop, knee,
Was the bottom of the
deep blue sea,
chop, knee.

☆ *This clapping song gets faster and faster. Clap each other's hands until SEA, clap your own hands at CHOP and pat your knees at KNEE.*

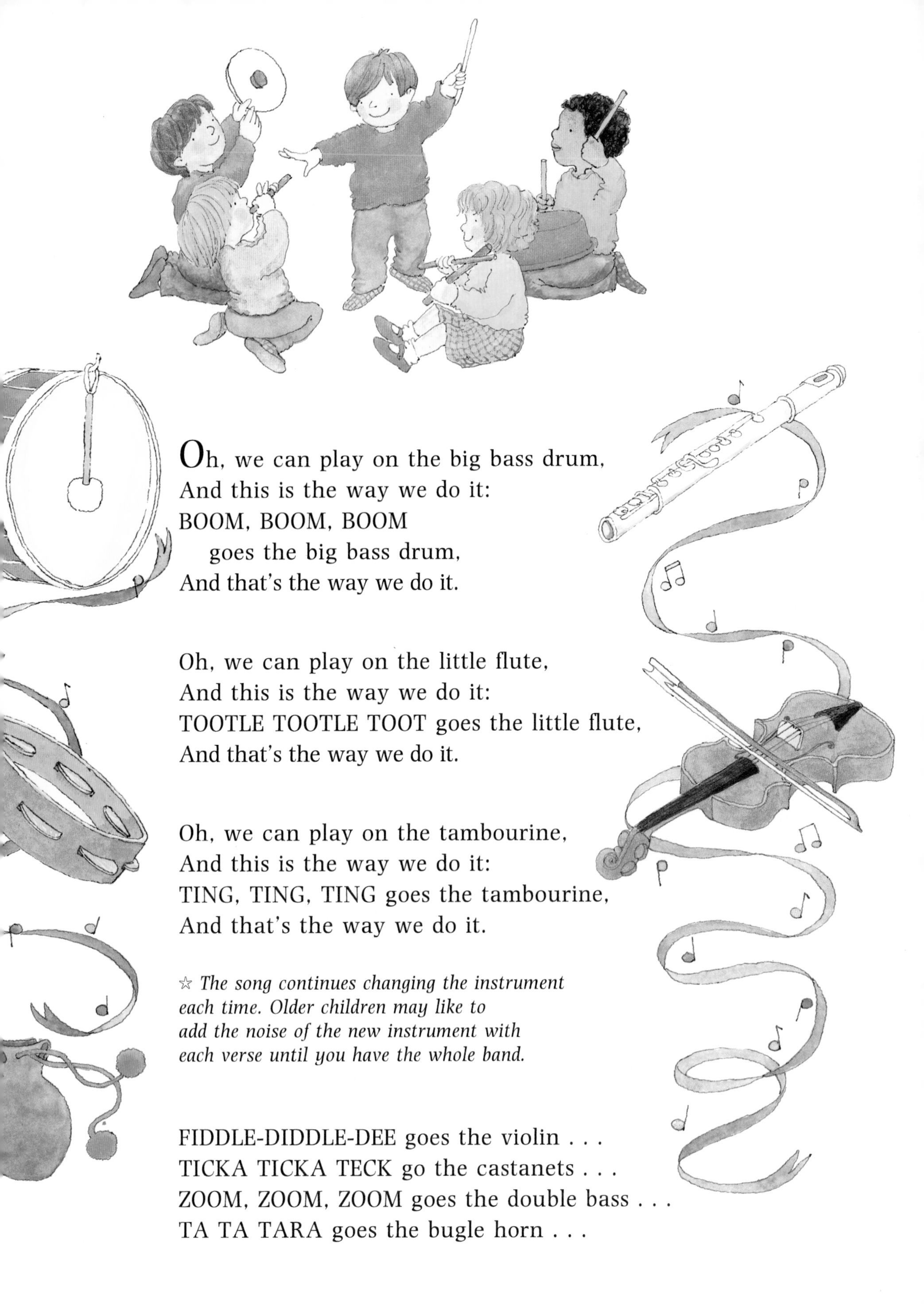

Oh, we can play on the big bass drum,
And this is the way we do it:
BOOM, BOOM, BOOM
goes the big bass drum,
And that's the way we do it.

Oh, we can play on the little flute,
And this is the way we do it:
TOOTLE TOOTLE TOOT goes the little flute,
And that's the way we do it.

Oh, we can play on the tambourine,
And this is the way we do it:
TING, TING, TING goes the tambourine,
And that's the way we do it.

☆ *The song continues changing the instrument each time. Older children may like to add the noise of the new instrument with each verse until you have the whole band.*

FIDDLE-DIDDLE-DEE goes the violin . . .
TICKA TICKA TECK go the castanets . . .
ZOOM, ZOOM, ZOOM goes the double bass . . .
TA TA TARA goes the bugle horn . . .

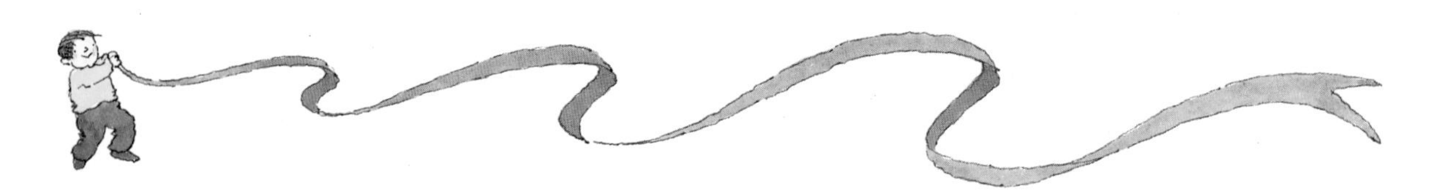

See-saw, Margery Daw,
Johnny shall have a new master;
He shall have but a penny a day,
Because he can't work any faster.

Sally go round the sun,
Sally go round the moon,
Sally go round the chimney-pots
On a Saturday afternoon.

☆ *A good swinging rhyme. Also a favourite for ring dancing.*

Swing me low
Swing me high,
Over the grasses
As high as the sky.
Hair flying out
Wind rushing by,
Like birds in the blue,
We sing as we fly,
Higher . . .
Fly . . .

☆ *Skipping rhymes.*

What's your name?
Johnny Maclean.
Where do you live?
Down the lane.
What's your shop?
Lollypop.
What's your number?
Cucumber.

What's your name?
Mary Jane.
Where do you live?
Cabbage Lane.
What's your number?
Rain and thunder.
What address?
Watercress.

The wood was dark
The grass was green,
Up comes Sally
With a tambourine.
Alpaca frock,
New scarf-shawl,
White straw bonnet
And a pink parasol.

I went to the river
No ship to get across,
I paid ten shillings
For an old blind horse.
I up on his back
And off in a crack,
Sally, tell my mother
I shall never come back.

Oranges and lemons,
Say the bells of St. Clements.

I owe you five farthings,
Say the bells of St. Martins.

When will you pay me?
Say the bells of Old Bailey.

When I grow rich,
Say the bells at Shoreditch.

When will that be?
Say the bells of Stepney.

I'm sure I don't know,
Says the great bell at Bow.

Here-comes-a-candle-to-light-you-to-bed,
Here-comes-a-chopper-to-chop-off-your-head,
Chip-chop-chip-chop-the-last-man's . . . HEAD

London Bridge is falling down,
Falling down, falling down,
London Bridge is falling down,
My fair lady.

Build it up with iron bars,
Iron bars, iron bars,
Build it up with iron bars,
My fair lady.

Here's a prisoner I have got,
I have got, I have got,
Here's a prisoner I have got,
My fair lady.

☆ *You need at least six children for these two games. Choose London Bridge for younger or more shy children.*

Two children form an arch (or two adults if the children are too short!); the others skip in a circle passing under the arch until the last lines.

For Oranges and Lemons the arch then pretends to chop the children as they pass through at CHIP and CHOP and captures one in their arms at HEAD.

The two sides of the arch are the Oranges and the Lemons, and the captive is asked to choose which he wants to be. This is done in secret so that the others don't know which side is which.

For London Bridge, a child is trapped at HERE'S A PRISONER and chooses to stand behind one of the people forming the arch.

The game is repeated until everyone has been caught. Then the two teams behind each side of the arch have a tug of war.

I'm a little teapot,
Short and stout,
Here's my handle,
Here's my spout.
When I see the teacups,
Hear me shout:
Tip me up and pour me out!

☆ *Do the actions as you sing.*

I can tie my shoelaces,
I can brush my hair,
I can wash my face and hands
And dry myself with care.

I can clean my teeth, too,
And fasten up my frocks,
I can dress all by myself
And pull up both my socks.

The Farmer's in the den,
The Farmer's in the den,
Eee-Aye-Eee-Aye,
The Farmer's in the den.

The Farmer wants a Wife . . .
The Wife wants a Child . . .
The Child wants a Nurse . . .
The Nurse wants a Dog . . .
The Dog wants a Bone . . .

We all pat the Bone,
We all pat the Bone,
Eee-Aye-Eee-Aye,
We all pat the Bone.

☆ *A game for at least six children. One child is chosen to be the farmer and the others join hands and dance around him as they sing. They stop for the farmer to choose a wife, who joins him inside the ring. The circle dances round again for the next verse, and so on until everybody pats the person who is the Bone.*

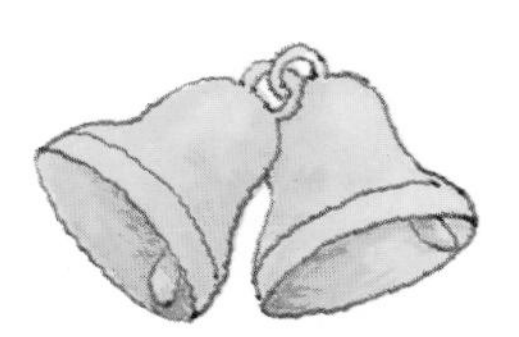

Frère Jacques, Frère Jacques,
Dormez-vous? Dormez-vous?
Sonnez les matines,
Sonnez les matines,
Din, din, don! Din, din, don!

I hear thunder, I hear thunder.
Hark, don't you? Hark, don't you?
  Pitter patter raindrops,
  Pitter patter raindrops,
I'm wet through, so are you.

☆ *Drum with hands or feet; stop and listen; flutter fingers; then hug as if cold.*

I see blue skies, I see blue skies,
Way up high, way up high.
  Hurry up now sunshine,
  Hurry up now sunshine,
I'll soon dry, I'll soon dry.

☆ *Look up and point to the sky; make the circle of the sun and shake hands dry.*

The wheels on the bus go round and round,
Round and round, round and round.
The wheels on the bus go round and round,
All day long.

☆ *Rotate arms like wheels.*

The wipers on the bus go:
Swish, swish, swish . . .

☆ *Wave hands from side to side.*

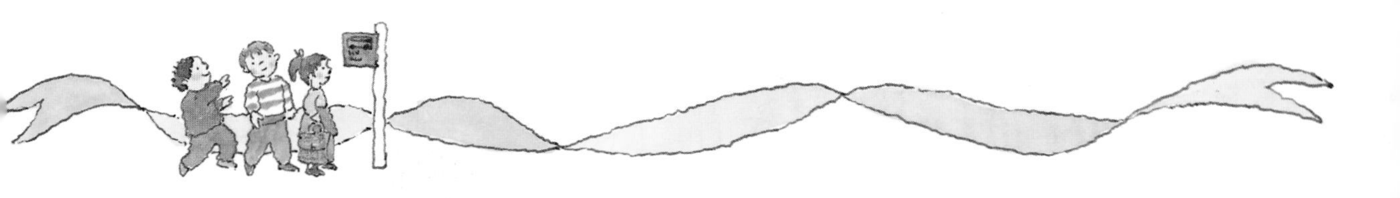

The driver on the bus goes:
Toot, toot, toot . . .

☆ *Press an imaginary horn with thumb.*

The people on the bus go:
Yakkity-yak! . . .

☆ *Open and shut fingers.*

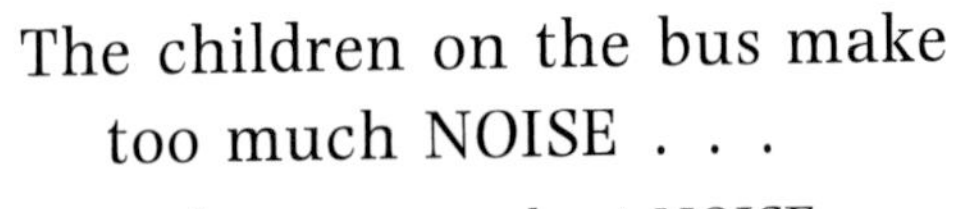

The children on the bus make
too much NOISE . . .

☆ *Hands over ears, shout NOISE.*

The babies on the bus
fall fast asleep . . .

☆ *Head on hands as if asleep and whisper lines.*

Here we go looby-loo,
Here we go looby-light,
Here we go looby-loo,
All on a Saturday night.

Put your right hand in,
Put your right hand out,
Shake it a little, a little,
And turn your self about.

Put your left hand in . . .
Put your right foot in . . .
Put your left foot in . . .
Put your whole self in . . .

☆ *Join hands and dance in a circle. Stop to do the actions of the second verse, and so on, repeating the first verse and dance after each new verse.*

Three times round went our gallant, gallant ship,
And three times round went she;
Three times round went our gallant, gallant ship,
Till she sank to the bottom of the sea.

☆ *Join hands and dance in a circle. Everybody falls down at the last line.*

Pull her up, pull her up, said the little sailor boy,
  Pull her up, pull her up, said he,
Pull her up, pull her up, said the little sailor boy,
  Or she'll sink to the bottom of the sea.

☆ *Still holding hands, pull each other up again.*

I sent a letter to my love
And on the way I dropped it,
A little puppy picked it up
And put it in his pocket.
It isn't you, it isn't you,
  But it is you.

☆ *The children stand or sit in a circle. One child has been chosen to be "it" and walks around the circle. On "it is you" he drops the letter (any small object) behind a child. That child picks it up and races around in the opposite direction to get back to his place before the first child reaches it. Whoever is left out becomes "it".*

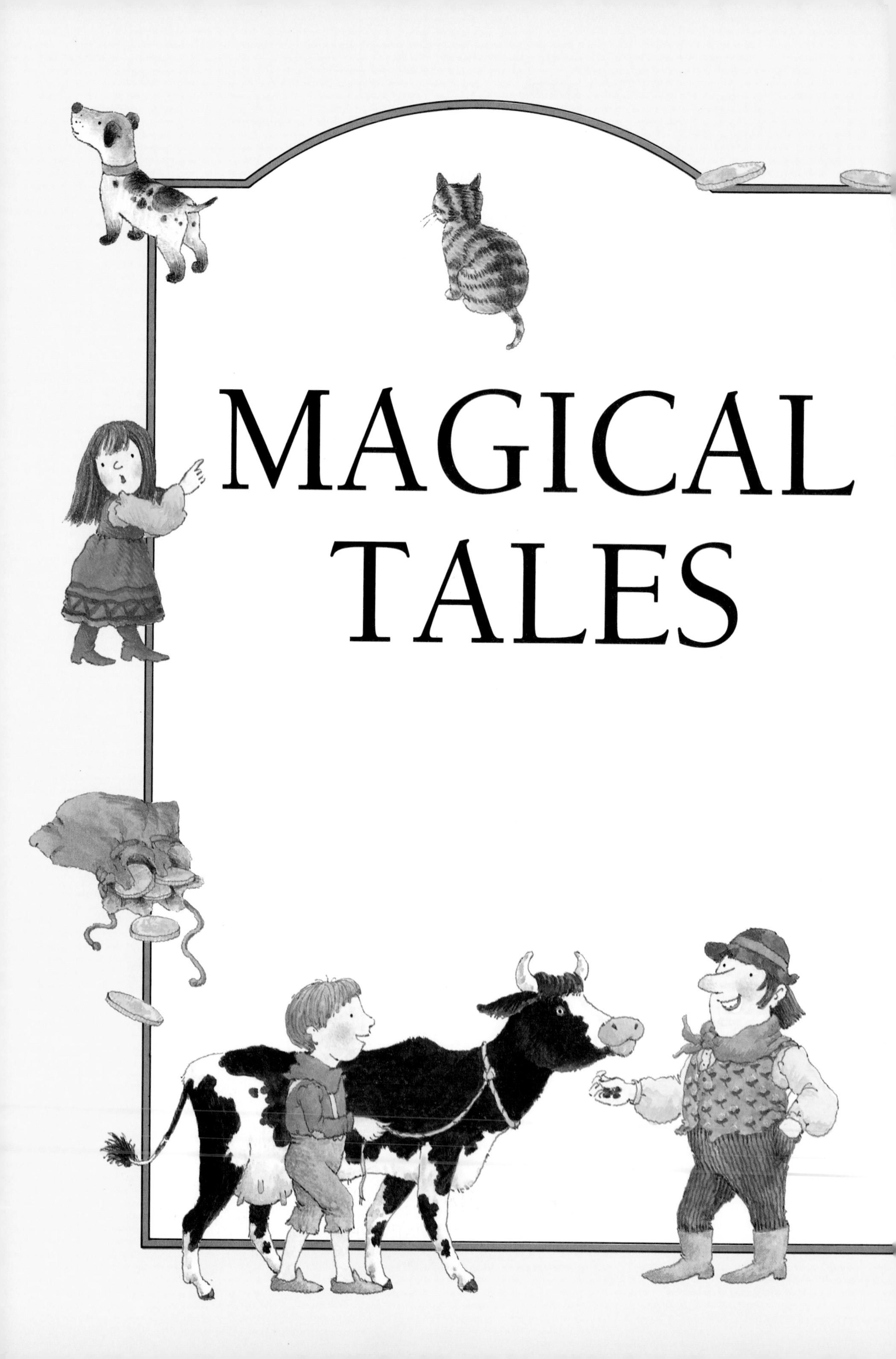

MAGICAL TALES

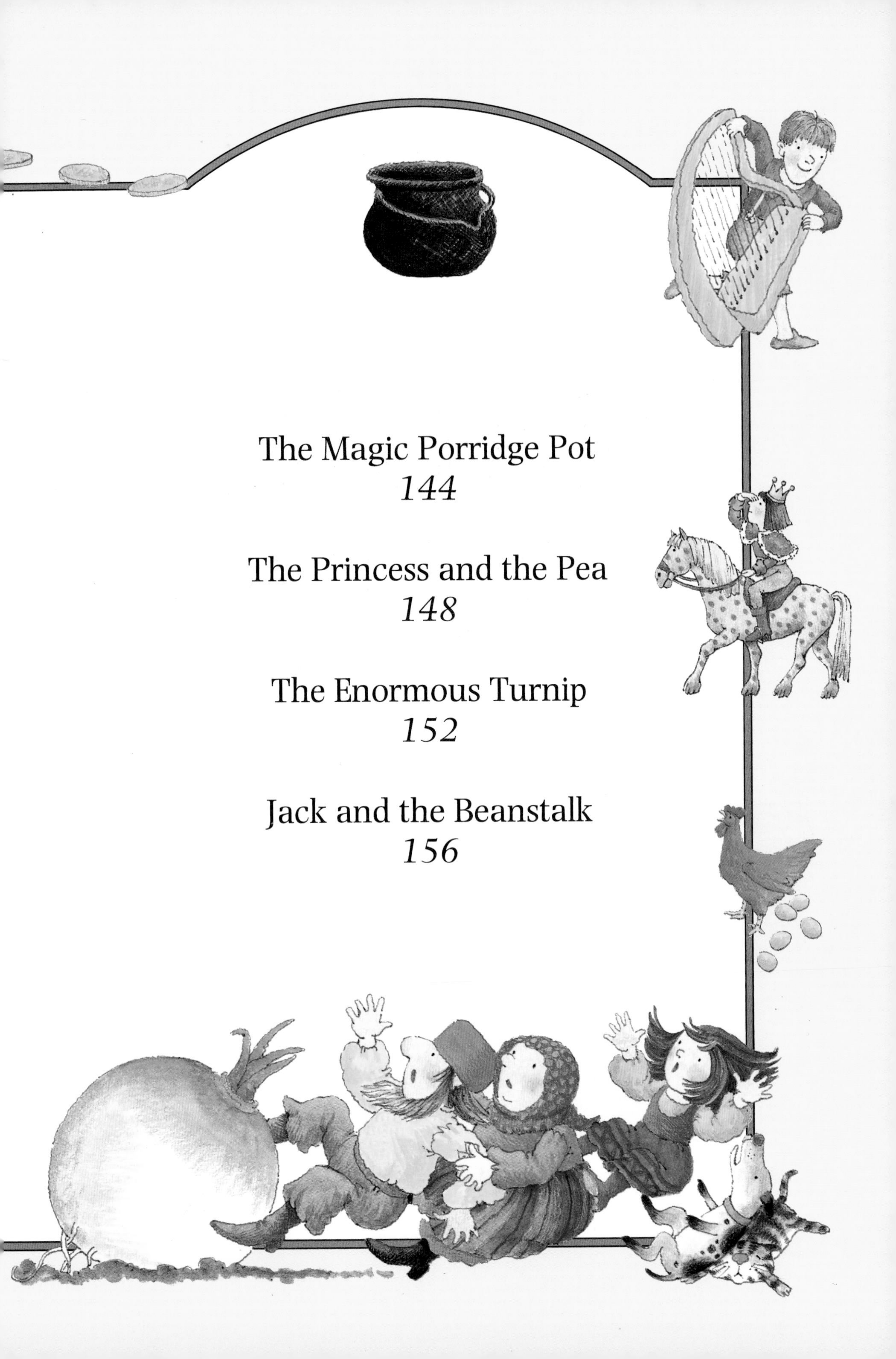

The Magic Porridge Pot
144

The Princess and the Pea
148

The Enormous Turnip
152

Jack and the Beanstalk
156

The Magic Porridge Pot

There was once a little girl who lived with her mother. They had no money and couldn't buy anything to eat. They were hungry all the time.

One day, all the mother had to give the little girl for her dinner was one thin biscuit. "Make it last," she said.

The little girl was playing in the street when along came a thin old man. "I haven't tasted a single mouthful of food in three days," he said. "Can you give me something to eat?"

The little girl felt so sorry for the thin old man that she gave him her biscuit.

"You are kind," said the old man, "and I am going to give you a present." From the pack on his back he took a little iron pot. "This is a magic pot. It won't work for me, but it will for you. When you want to eat, all you have to say is 'Little pot, cook!' and the pot will fill itself with hot porridge. When you've eaten all you want, just say 'Little pot, enough!' and it will stop."

The little girl ran home with the pot and put it on the table. She called her mother and said, "Little pot, cook!"

Straight away the little pot filled with hot porridge, already mixed with milk and sugar. The little girl and her mother ate three bowls each and felt full and happy. Then the little girl said, "Little pot, enough!" and the pot stopped making porridge.

The girl and her mother were never hungry after that.

But one day the little girl was out playing and the mother wanted some porridge. "I won't call her in from her game," she thought. "I know what to say." And she said, "Cook, little pot!"

Nothing happened.

"Oh, wrong way round. Little pot, cook!"

The little pot filled itself with porridge. The mother ate a big bowlful and, while she was eating, the little pot was filling itself up again.

The mother didn't want any more, so she said, "Stop, little pot!"

The pot went on filling – and it filled quickly!

"Little pot, stop!"

Porridge began running over the top of the pot.

"Little pot, no more!"

Porridge poured from the pot, over the table and onto the floor.

"No more, little pot!"

The floor was ankle-deep in gooey porridge.

"Oh, what are the right words? Porridge pot, stop!"

Faster and faster came the porridge, rising up the walls, burying the chairs. The mother opened the door and porridge began running down the street.

"Stop, porridge pot!"

But nothing the mother could think of to say stopped the porridge. It poured down the street and swept a cat off its feet. It ran into other houses and clogged the wheels of cars and bicycles. There was porridge everywhere!

The little girl was coming home when she saw a stream of

porridge coming towards her carrying along cats and dogs and babies. She guessed what had happened.

She shouted, "Little pot, enough!"

The pot heard her and stopped.

Then everyone had to bring spoons and eat themselves into house and home.

The Princess and the Pea

Once upon a time there was a prince who wanted to marry a princess; but she had to be a *real* princess. He travelled all over the world in his search for a princess, and princesses he found in plenty; but whether they were *real* princesses he couldn't decide, for now one thing, now another, seemed not quite right. Sadly he returned home to his palace – he wanted so much to have a real princess for his wife.

One evening there was a fearful storm; thunder crashed, lightning flashed, rain poured down from the sky in torrents and it was dark as dark can be. All at once there was heard a knocking at the door. The prince's father, the old king himself, went to open it.

A princess stood outside; but gracious! what a sight she was, standing out there in the rain. Water trickled down from her hair, water dripped from her clothes, water ran in at the toes of her shoes and out at the heels. And yet she said she was a real princess.

"We shall soon see about that!" thought the old queen, but she didn't say anything.

She went into the bedroom, took all the clothes off the bed and laid one dried pea on the mattress. Then she piled twenty more mattresses on top of it and twenty eiderdowns over the

twenty mattresses. On this the girl who said she was a real princess was to lie all night.

The next morning she was asked how she had slept.

"Oh, shockingly!" she replied. "I haven't even closed my eyes. I don't know what was in my bed, but there was something hard that has bruised me all over."

They saw at once that she must be a *real* princess, for she had felt the little dried pea through twenty eiderdowns and twenty mattresses. Only a *real* princess could have such delicate skin.

So the prince asked the princess to marry him and the pea was put in a museum as a curiosity. You may go yourself and see it.

Now, wasn't that a *real* story?

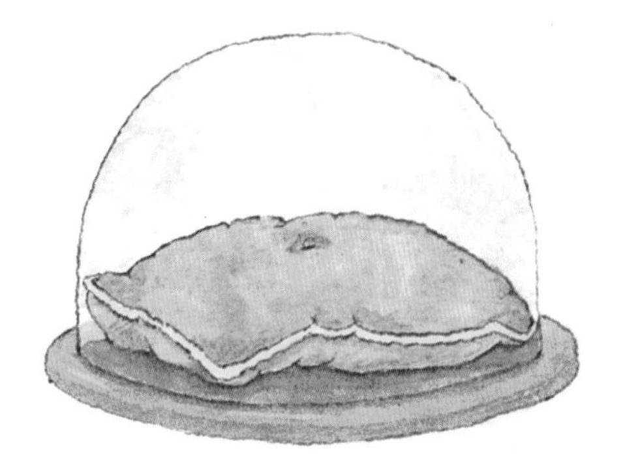

The Enormous Turnip

Once upon a time there was an old man who planted a turnip seed in the ground and waited for it to grow.

First it grew into a small turnip, then a middling turnip, then a big turnip, then a bigger turnip and then an enormous turnip! The old man decided that it was time to pull the turnip up and eat it.

So he took hold of the turnip and pulled. But the turnip stayed in the ground.

The old man took a better grip and pulled harder. The turnip still stayed in the ground.

Then the old man gritted his teeth and pulled and pulled and pulled, until he had no pull left in him. But the turnip stayed in the ground.

So the old man went to his wife and said, "Wife, come and help me pull up this turnip."

So the old woman went with him back to the turnip. She took hold of the old man, the old man took hold of the turnip and they pulled. They pulled again.

They pulled and they pulled and they pulled, until they had no pull left in them. And the turnip stayed in the ground.

So the old woman went and found her granddaughter and said, "Granddaughter, come and help us pull up this turnip."

The granddaughter went back with the old woman. She took hold of the old woman, the old woman took hold of the old man, the old man took hold of the turnip and they all got ready.

"Now, let's try tugging," said the old man.

So they tugged.

They TUGGED and TUGGED and TUGGED, until none of them had any tug left. And the turnip stayed in the ground.

So the granddaughter went and found the dog.

"Dog," she said, "come and help us tug this turnip up."

The dog went with the girl back to the turnip. The dog took hold of the girl, the girl took hold of the old woman, the old woman took hold of the old man, the old man took hold of the turnip and they all got ready.

"Let's try heaving," said the old man.

So they heaved at the turnip.

They HEAVED and they HEAVED and they HEAVED.

HEAVE . . .

HEAVE . . .

HEAVE . . . until none of them had any heave left in them. And the turnip stayed in the ground.

So the dog went away and found the cat and said, "Cat, come and help us heave at this turnip."

The cat went with the dog and took hold of the dog. The dog took hold of the girl, the girl took hold of the old woman, the old woman took hold of the old man, the old man took hold of the turnip and they all got ready.

"Let's try dragging it this time."

So they dragged at the turnip.

They dragged again.

They dragged one last time.

And UP came the turnip out of the ground!

And the cat fell on the ground, the dog fell on the cat, the girl fell on the dog, the old woman fell on her granddaughter, the old man fell on his wife and the turnip fell on the old man.

It took all of them to pull, tug, heave and drag the turnip to the house. There they cut it up and made it into turnip soup. There was more than enough for everyone and, for all I know, the old man, the old woman, their granddaughter, the dog and the cat have lived on turnip soup from that day to this and are all eating huge bowlfuls of turnip soup this very minute, even as you are listening to this story.

But that's enough of turnips, and the end of the story.

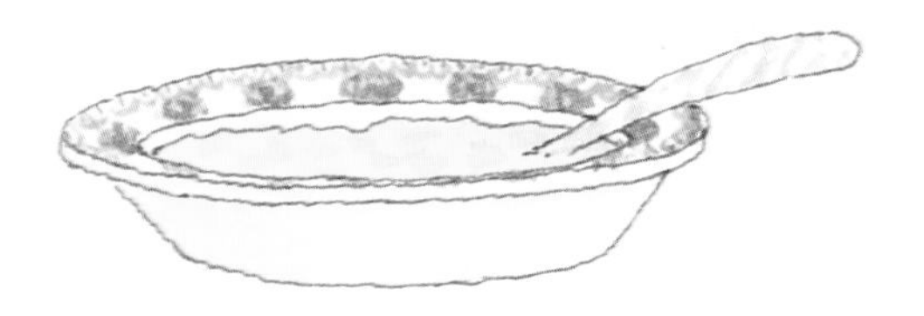

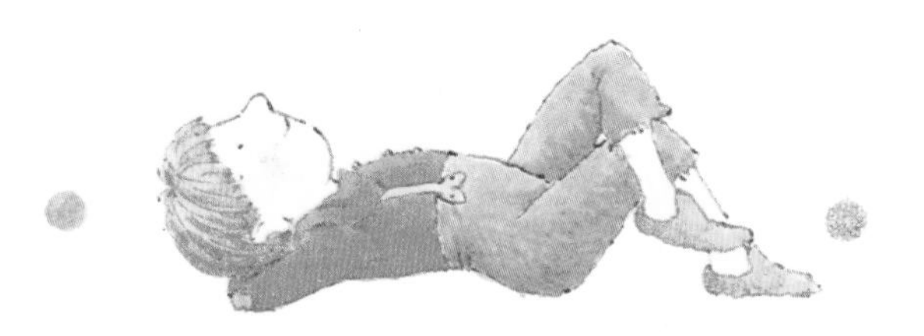

Jack and the Beanstalk

Once upon a time there was a poor widow who had one son and his name was Jack. Jack was no help to his mother because he was lazy and only wanted to lie in front of the fire all day.

"You never do anything," she always said to him. "And when you do, you never do it right!"

Jack and his mother had no money at all and the only valuable thing they owned was their old cow.

"I don't want to sell the old cow," said Jack's mother, "because she gives us milk, but I don't see what else we can do. Jack, take the old cow to market and sell her for the highest price you can get."

It was a long walk to market and Jack didn't want to go, but he had no choice. He tied a rope around the old cow's neck and set off, as slowly as he could.

He hadn't gone very far when he met a man.

"That's a stringy old thing of a cow," the man said. "Where are you taking her?"

"To market, to sell her," said Jack.

"You won't get much for that old thing," said the man. "How much are you asking for her?"

"How much are you offering?" asked Jack.

The man put his hand in his pocket and pulled something out. "Five beans – and you won't get any more for that old creature at market!"

"That may be," said Jack, "but my mother will be furious if I go home with nothing but five beans. Even five pennies would be better."

"But these are magic beans," said the man. "They will make your fortune."

"Done!" said Jack, because he really couldn't be bothered to walk all the way to market. So the man gave him the five beans and Jack gave the man the cow and then he went home, feeling pleased because he hadn't had to walk very far.

"Back already?" said his mother. "What did you get for the cow?"

Jack took the beans from his pocket and showed them to his mother. "Beans!" she said. "Five beans! Why, you useless great lump!" She threw the beans out of the window. Then she sent Jack to bed. He didn't even get a chance to explain that the beans were magic and would make their fortune.

When Jack woke up the next morning, the house was dark, as if it were still night, and there was a rustling, creeping noise. The beans that Jack's mother had thrown out of the window had grown overnight into a huge beanstalk. The stem was so thick that it was blocking the window, and it was growing so fast that the leaves made a rustling, creeping noise as they pushed upwards.

Jack ran outside and saw that the beanstalk grew up and up until it disappeared into the clouds. "They *were* magic beans," Jack said to himself. "I wonder what's up there." He started to climb the beanstalk to find out what was at the top.

Jack climbed up and up and up, all the way to the top. There he found a path that led through the clouds to a great big castle.

Jack knocked on the door. A huge woman opened it. She looked surprised to see him.

"What are you doing here?" she asked. "Don't you know that a giant lives here, a giant who eats little boys?"

Jack said, "But I've climbed so high and walked so far. I'm hungry – thirsty too."

"Alright, come in," said the woman. "But you mustn't stay long."

Inside the castle, Jack and the woman got talking. Before they knew it, noisy footsteps were coming up the path.

"It's my husband, the giant!" said the woman. "Quick! Hide!"

Jack jumped into an empty pot by the stove and pulled down the lid just as the door opened and the giant walked in.

The giant sniffed the air and said:

"Fee, fi, fo, fum,

I smell the blood of an Englishman.

Be he alive or be he dead,

I'll grind his bones to make my bread!"

"How you go on," said the giant's wife. "There's no one here. Now sit down and eat your dinner."

So the giant sat down and ate his dinner. Then he took out a grubby-looking purse, opened it and tipped it upside-down. Out fell a great heap of gold. The giant closed the purse, opened it again – and it was filled with gold once more!

Jack was peeping out of his pot and saw.

"If my mother and I had that purse," he thought, "we'd never be poor again." He made up his mind that he was going to take that purse home with him, come what may.

He watched and waited until the giant went over to his chair in front of the fire, kicked off his boots and went to sleep. Then Jack crept out of the pot, grabbed the purse and ran for his life!

Out of the castle he ran, along the path, down the beanstalk and into his house, shouting, "Mother! Mother! Look!"

Jack's mother was amazed that her lazy son had been so brave. She looked at the purse and said, "We shall never be poor again. Promise me that you won't climb the beanstalk any more. It's dangerous."

Jack promised he wouldn't.

With the money that the purse gave them, Jack and his mother were much happier than before, but Jack couldn't forget the castle. One day, while his mother was out, he climbed the beanstalk again.

When Jack knocked on the castle door, the giant's wife opened it and said, "You again! If the giant finds you here . . . well, he'll eat you raw!"

"Oh, I'll be long gone before he gets back," Jack said. "But I must have a sit-down and something to eat and drink. I've come such a long way."

The kind woman took him in. Jack wanted to stay until the giant came home, so he got her talking until she forgot all about the time passing.

Then they heard the giant coming home.

Jack opened the cupboard under the sink and crawled inside. In came the giant, sniffing the air.

"Fee, fi, fo, fum,

I smell the blood of an Englishman.

Be he alive or be he dead,

I'll have his blood to sauce my bread!"

"Oh, don't go on," said the giant's wife. "There's no one here. Eat your food, you big lump."

So the giant sat down to his dinner. When he'd finished, he brought out a beautiful red hen. He stroked her feathers gently and the hen laid eggs for him. Not ordinary eggs, but eggs of beautiful shining gold!

Jack waited until the giant had fallen asleep by the fire. Then he crept out of the cupboard, grabbed the hen and ran for his life!

Out of the castle, along the path, down the beanstalk and into his house he ran, shouting, "Mother! Mother! Look!"

When Jack's mother saw the hen and the eggs, she could hardly believe her eyes. She made him promise, *promise*, never to climb the beanstalk again.

Jack promised.

With all the gold from the purse and the golden eggs from the hen, they were rich. But Jack couldn't forget the castle. He went out and climbed the beanstalk once more.

When the giant's wife opened the door and saw who it was, she said, "Go away! I dare not let you in." But she was a kind woman and Jack persuaded her to let him in after all. They got talking and the giant's wife soon forgot all about the time – until she heard her husband coming home.

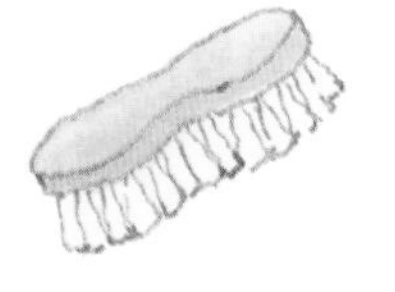

Jack crawled under the washtub and hid. In came the giant, sniffing the air.

"Fee, fi, fo, fum,

I smell the blood of an Englishman . . ."

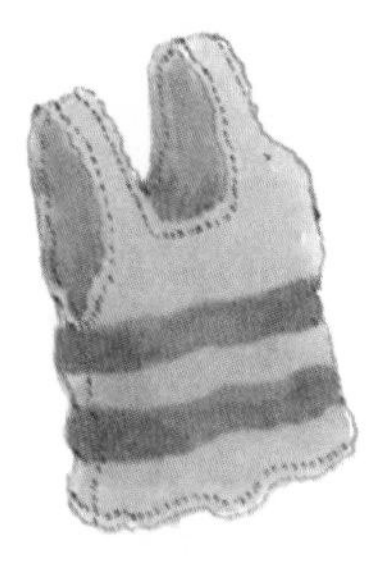

"Oh, get away with you," said his wife. "Sit down and have your dinner."

When the giant had eaten his dinner, he fetched a beautiful golden harp. "Play, Harp," he said, and the harp played beautiful music, all by itself!

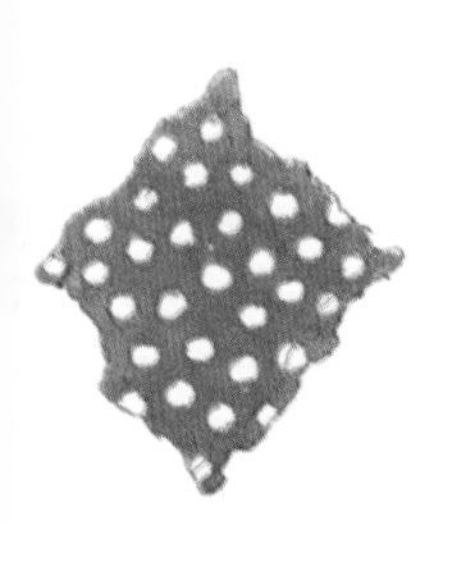

Jack waited until the giant fell asleep by the fire, then he crept out, grabbed the golden harp and ran for his life!

But, as he ran, the harp cried out, "Master! Master!" The giant woke up, jumped to his feet and ran after Jack with great big strides.

Jack reached the beanstalk first and started climbing down as fast as he could. But the giant reached the beanstalk too and began climbing down after him.

Jack reached the ground first, dropped the harp and snatched up an axe his mother used to chop wood. He began to chop down the beanstalk.

He chopped and chopped and chopped until at last he chopped right through. Down came the beanstalk, and down came the giant. With a CRASH! the giant landed on his head and that was the end of him.

So Jack and his mother had the purse of gold and the hen that laid golden eggs and the harp that played all by itself, and they lived happily in comfort all the rest of their lives.

And that is the end of the story.

A WAS AN APPLE PIE

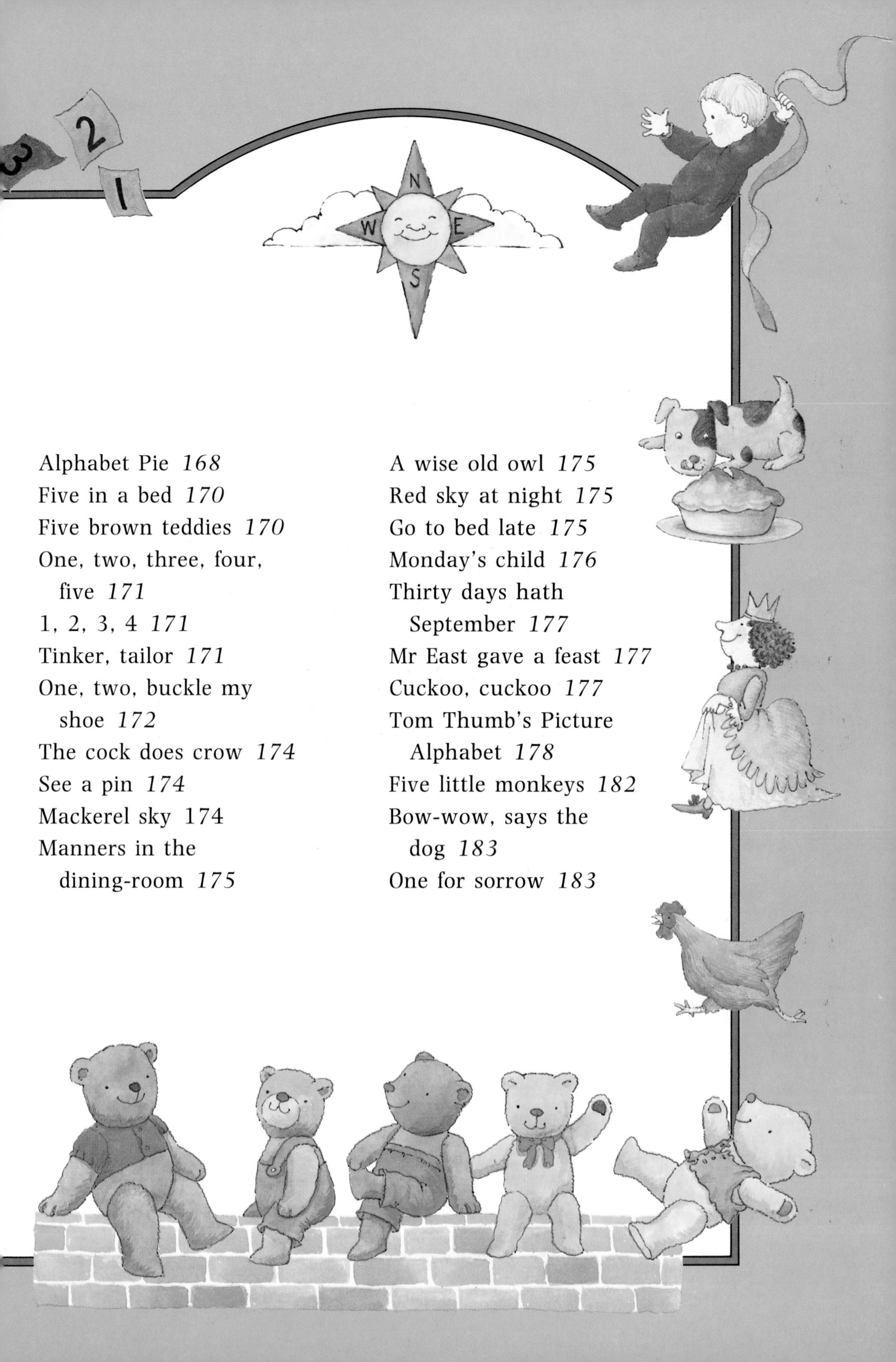

Alphabet Pie *168*
Five in a bed *170*
Five brown teddies *170*
One, two, three, four, five *171*
1, 2, 3, 4 *171*
Tinker, tailor *171*
One, two, buckle my shoe *172*
The cock does crow *174*
See a pin *174*
Mackerel sky 174
Manners in the dining-room *175*
A wise old owl *175*
Red sky at night *175*
Go to bed late *175*
Monday's child *176*
Thirty days hath September *177*
Mr East gave a feast *177*
Cuckoo, cuckoo *177*
Tom Thumb's Picture Alphabet *178*
Five little monkeys *182*
Bow-wow, says the dog *183*
One for sorrow *183*

Alphabet Pie

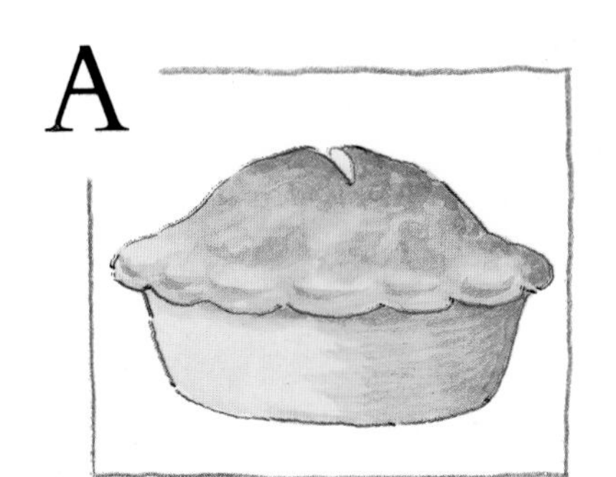

A was an apple pie

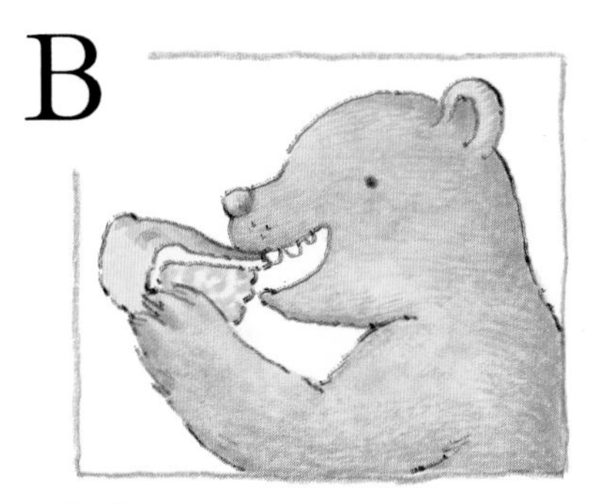

B bit it

C cut it

D dealt it

E eat it

F fought for it

G got it

H had it

I inspected it

J jumped for it

K kept it

L longed for it

ABCDEFGHIJKLMNOPQRSTUVWXYZ

M

M mourned for it

N

N nodded at it

O

O opened it

P

P peeped in it

Q

Q quartered it

R

R ran for it

S

S sang for it

T

T took it

U

U upset it

V

V viewed it

W

W wanted it

XYZ

XYZ and **&** all wished for a piece in hand.

There were five in the bed and
the little one said: Roll over! Roll over!
So they all rolled over and one fell out.

There were four in the bed . . .
There were three in the bed . . .
There were two in the bed . . .

There was one in the bed,
And that little one said:
Good, now I've got the
bed to myself, I'm going
to stretch and stretch
and stretch!

☆ *Both of these rhymes can be played with five children or toys.*

Five brown teddies sitting on a wall,
Five brown teddies sitting on a wall,
And if one brown teddy should accidentally fall,
There'd be four brown teddies sitting on a wall.

Four brown teddies sitting on a wall . . .
Three brown teddies sitting on a wall . . .
Two brown teddies sitting on a wall . . .
One brown teddy sitting on a wall,
One brown teddy sitting on a wall,
And if one brown teddy should accidentally fall,
There'd be no brown teddies sitting there at all!

♫ *Sing to a the tune of "Ten Green Bottles".*

One two, three, four, five,
Once I caught a fish alive,
Six, seven, eight, nine, ten,
Then I threw it back again.
Why did you let it go?
Because it bit my finger so.
Which finger did it bite?
This little finger on the right.

1 2, 3, 4,
Mary at the kitchen door,
5, 6, 7, 8,
Counting cherries off a plate.

Tinker,
Tailor,
Soldier,
Sailor,
Richman,
Poorman,
Beggarman,
Thief.
Lady,
Baby,
Gipsey,
Queen.
This year,
Next year,
Sometime,
Never.

One, two,
Buckle my shoe;

Three, four,
Knock at the door;

Five, six,
Pick up sticks;

Seven, eight,
Lay them straight;

Nine, ten,
A big fat hen;

Eleven, twelve,
Dig and delve;

Thirteen, fourteen,
Maids a-courting;

Fifteen, sixteen,
Maids in the kitchen;

Seventeen, eighteen,
Maids in waiting;

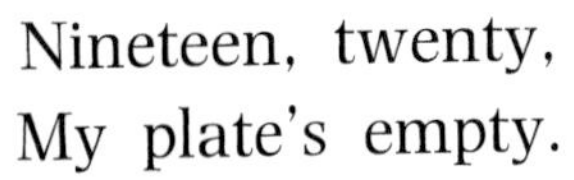

Nineteen, twenty,
My plate's empty.

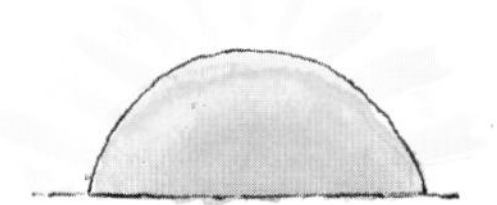

The cock does crow
To let you know
If you be wise
'Tis time to rise;
For early to bed
And early to rise
Is the way to be healthy
And wealthy and wise.

See a pin and pick it up,
All the day you'll have good luck.
See a pin and let it lay,
Bad luck you'll have all the day.

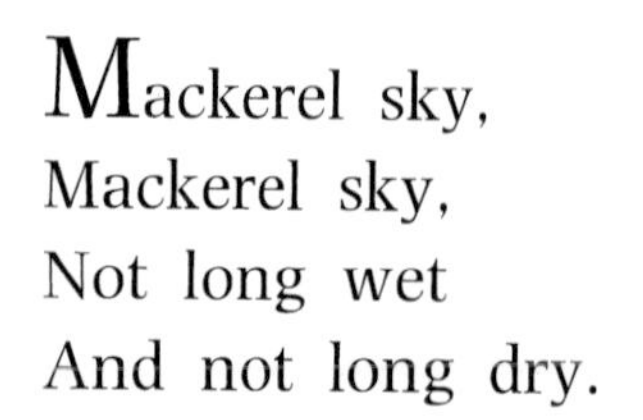

Mackerel sky,
Mackerel sky,
Not long wet
And not long dry.

Manners in the dining-room,
  Manners in the hall,
If you don't behave yourself
  You shan't have none at all.

A wise old owl sat in an oak,
The more he heard the less he spoke;
The less he spoke the more he heard.
Why aren't we all like that wise old bird?

Red sky at night,
  Shepherd's delight;
Red sky in the morning,
  Shepherd's warning.

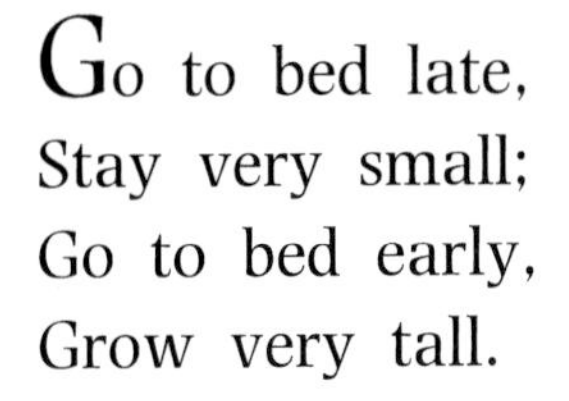

Go to bed late,
Stay very small;
Go to bed early,
Grow very tall.

Monday's child
is fair of face,

Tuesday's child
is full of grace,

Wednesday's child
is full of woe,

Thursday's child
has far to go,

Friday's child
is loving and giving,

Saturday's child
works hard for
his living,

And the child that's born on the Sabbath day
Is bonny and blithe, and good and gay.

Thirty days hath September,
April, June, and November;
All the rest have thirty-one,
Excepting February alone;
And that has twenty-eight days clear
And twenty-nine in each leap year.

Mr East gave a feast;
Mr North laid the cloth;
Mr West did his best;
Mr South burnt his mouth
With eating a cold potato.

Cuckoo, cuckoo, what do you do?
In April I open my bill;
In May I sing all day;
In June I change my tune;
In July away I fly;
In August away I must.

Tom Thumb's Picture Alphabet

A was an archer
and shot at a
frog;

B was a butcher
and had a
great dog.

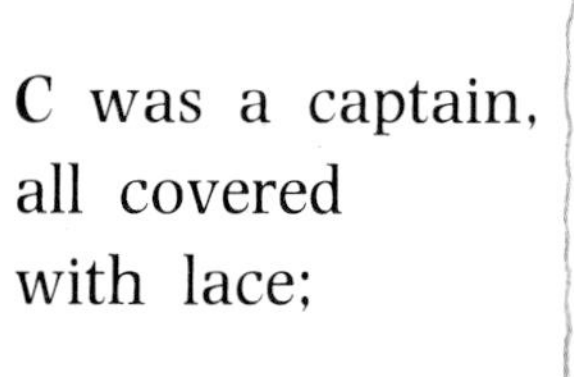

C was a captain,
all covered
with lace;

D was a drummer
and had a
red face.

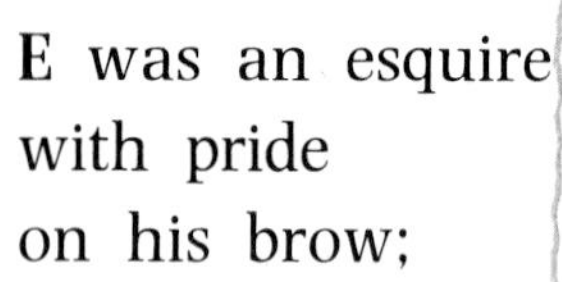

E was an esquire
with pride
on his brow;

F was a farmer
and followed
the plough.

G was a gamester
who had but
ill-luck;

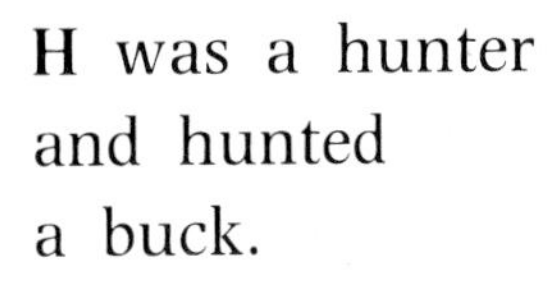

H was a hunter
and hunted
a buck.

I was an innkeeper
who loved
to carouse;

J was a joiner
and built up
a house.

K was a king,
so mighty
and grand;

L was a lady
and had a
white hand.

M was a miser
and hoarded
up gold;

N was a
nobleman,
gallant
and bold.

O was an oyster
girl and went
about town;

P was a parson
and wore a
black gown.

Q was a queen
who wore a
silk slip;

R was robber
and wanted
a whip.

S was a sailor
and spent all
he got;

T was a tinker
and mended
a pot.

U was a usurer,
a miserable
elf;

V was a vintner
who drank all
himself.

W was a watchman
and guarded
the door;

X was expensive
and so became
poor.

Y was a youth
and did not
love school;

Z was a zany,
a poor
harmless fool.

Five little monkeys walked
along the shore,

One went a'sailing,

Then there were four.

Four little monkeys
climbed up a tree,
One tumbled down,

Then there were three.

Three little monkeys found
a pot of glue,

One got stuck in it,

Then there were two.

Two little monkeys found
a currant bun,

One ran away with it,

Then there was one,

One little monkey
and his little wife,
Lived in a banana tree
for the rest of his life.

Bow-wow, says the dog,
Mew, mew, says the cat,
Grunt, grunt, goes the hog,
And squeak goes the rat.
Tu-whu, says the owl,
Caw, caw, says the crow,
Quack, quack, says the duck,
And what cuckoos say you know.

One for sorrow, two for joy,
Three for a girl, four for a boy,
Five for silver, six for gold,
Seven for a secret ne'er to be told.

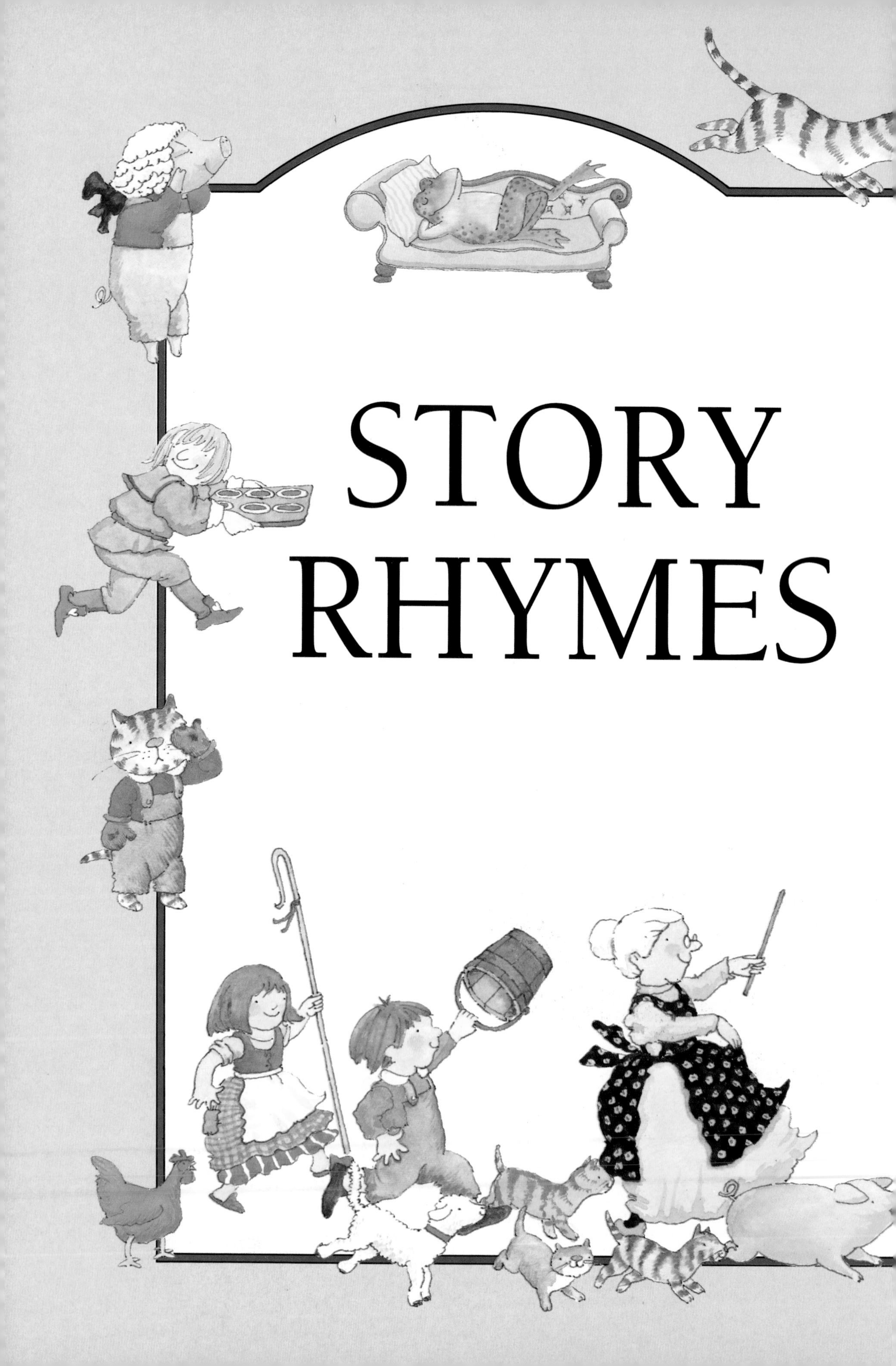

STORY RHYMES

Mary had a little lamb *186*
Jack and Jill *187*
Three little kittens *188*
Little Piggy *190*
The Queen of Hearts *192*
Pussy cat, pussy cat *193*
The Owl and the Pussy Cat *194*
Little Bo-peep *196*
Little Miss Muffet *197*
Once a Mouse, a Frog and a Little Red Hen *198*
Old Mother Hubbard *200*

Mary had a little lamb,
Its fleece was white as snow;
And everywhere that Mary went
The lamb was sure to go.

It followed her to school one day,
That was against the rule;
It made the children laugh and play
To see a lamb at school.

And so the teacher turned it out,
But still it lingered near,
And waited patiently about
Till Mary did appear.

Why does the lamb love Mary so?
The eager children cry;
Why, Mary loves the lamb, you know,
The teacher did reply.

Jack and Jill
Went up the hill,
To fetch a pail of water;
Jack fell down,
And broke his crown,
And Jill came tumbling after.

Then up Jack got,
And home did trot,
As fast as he could caper;
To old Dame Dob,
Who patched his nob
With vinegar and brown paper.

Three little kittens
They lost their mittens,
And they began to cry,
Oh, Mother dear, we sadly fear
Our mittens we have lost.

What! lost your mittens,
You naughty kittens!
Then you shall have no pie.
  Mee-ow, mee-ow, mee-ow.
No, you shall have no pie.

The three little kittens
They found their mittens,
And they began to cry,
Oh, Mother dear,
  see here, see here,
Our mittens we have found.

Put on your mittens,
You silly kittens,
And you shall have some pie.
  Purr-r, purr-r, purr-r,
Oh, let us have some pie.

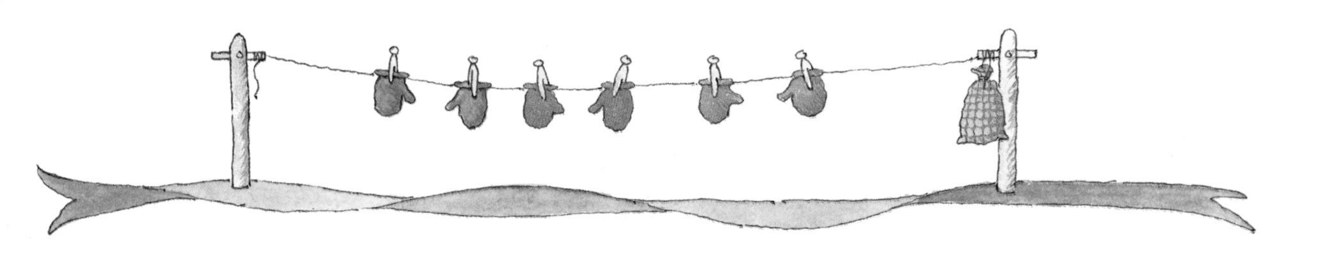

The three little kittens
Put on their mittens
And soon ate up the pie;
Oh, Mother dear, we greatly fear
Our mittens we have soiled.

What! soiled your mittens,
You naughty kittens!
Then they began to sigh,
Mee-ow, mee-ow, mee-ow,
Then they began to sigh.

The three little kittens
They washed their mittens,
And hung them out to dry;
Oh, Mother dear, do you not hear,
Our mittens we have washed.

What! washed your mittens,
You good little kittens,
But I smell a rat close by.
Mee-ow, mee-ow, mee-ow,
We smell a rat close by.

Little Piggy

Where are you going, you little pig?
I'm leaving my mother, I'm growing so big!
So big, young pig!
So young, so big!
What, leaving your mother,
You foolish young pig!

Where are you going, you little pig?
I've got a new spade, and I'm going to dig!
To dig, little pig!
A little pig dig!
Well, I never saw a pig with a spade
that could dig!

Where are you going, you little pig?
Why, I'm going to have a nice ride in a gig!
In a gig, little pig!
What, a pig in a gig!
Well, I never yet saw a pig in a gig!

Where are you going, you little pig?
I'm going to the barber's to buy me a wig!
    A wig, little pig!
    A pig in a wig!
Why, whoever before saw a pig in a wig!

Where are you going, you little pig?
Why, I'm going to the ball to dance a fine jig!
    A jig, little pig!
    A pig dance a jig!
Well, I never before saw a pig dance a jig!

THOMAS HOOD

The Queen of Hearts
She made some tarts,
All on a summer's day;
The Knave of Hearts
He stole the tarts,
And took them clean away.

The King of Hearts
Called for the tarts,
And beat the knave full sore;
The Knave of Hearts
Brought back the tarts,
And vowed he'd steal no more.

Pussy cat, pussy cat,
Where have you been?
I've been to London
To look at the Queen.

Pussy cat, pussy cat,
What did you there?
I frightened a little mouse
Under her chair.

The Owl and the Pussy Cat

The Owl and the Pussy Cat went to sea
   In a beautiful pea-green boat:
They took some honey, and plenty of money
   Wrapped up in a five-pound note.

The Owl looked up to the stars above,
   And sang to a small guitar,
"O lovely Pussy, O Pussy, my love,
   What a beautiful Pussy you are,
You are, you are!
   What a beautiful Pussy you are!"

Pussy said to the Owl, "You elegant fowl,
  How charmingly sweet you sing!
Oh! let us be married; too long we have tarried:
  But what shall we do for a ring?"

They sailed away, for a year and a day,
  To the land where the bong-tree grows;
And there in a wood a Piggy-wig stood,
  With a ring at the end of his nose,
His nose, his nose,
  With a ring at the end of his nose.

"Dear Pig, are you willing to sell for
  one shilling
  Your ring?" Said the Piggy, "I will."
So they took it away, and were married
  next day
  By the Turkey who lives on the hill.

They dined on mince and slices of quince,
  Which they ate with a runcible spoon;
And hand in hand, on the edge of the sand,
  They danced by the light of the moon,
The moon, the moon,
  They danced by the light of the moon.

EDWARD LEAR

Little Bo-peep has lost her sheep,
And can't tell where to find them;
Leave them alone, and they'll come home,
Bringing their tails behind them.

Little Bo-peep fell fast asleep,
And dreamt she heard them bleating;
But when she awoke, she found it a joke,
For they were still a-fleeting.

Then up she took her little crook,
Determined for to find them;
She found them indeed,
but it made her heart bleed,
For they'd left their tails behind them.

It happened one day, as Bo-peep did stray
Into a meadow hard by,
There she espied their tails side by side,
All hung on a tree to dry.

She heaved a sigh, and wiped her eye,
And over the hillocks went rambling,
And tried what she could,
as a shepherdess should,
To tack each again to its lambkin.

Little Miss Muffet
Sat on a tuffet,
Eating her curds and whey;
There came a big spider,
Who sat down beside her
And frightened Miss Muffet away.

Once a Mouse, a Frog,
and a Little Red Hen,
Together kept a house;
The Frog was the laziest of frogs,
And lazier still was the Mouse.

The work all fell on the Little Red Hen,
Who had to get the wood,
And build the fires, and scrub, and cook,
And sometimes hunt the food.

One day, as she went scratching round,
She found a bag of rye;
Said she, "Now who will make
some bread?"
Said the lazy Mouse, "Not I."

"Nor I," croaked the Frog
as he drowsed in the shade,
Red Hen made no reply,
But flew around with bowl and spoon,
And mixed and stirred the rye.

"Who'll make the fire to bake the bread?"
Said the Mouse again, "Not I,"
And, scarcely opening his
sleepy eyes,
Frog made the same reply.

The Little Red Hen said never a word,
But a roaring fire she made;
And while the bread was baking brown,
"Who'll set the table?" she said.

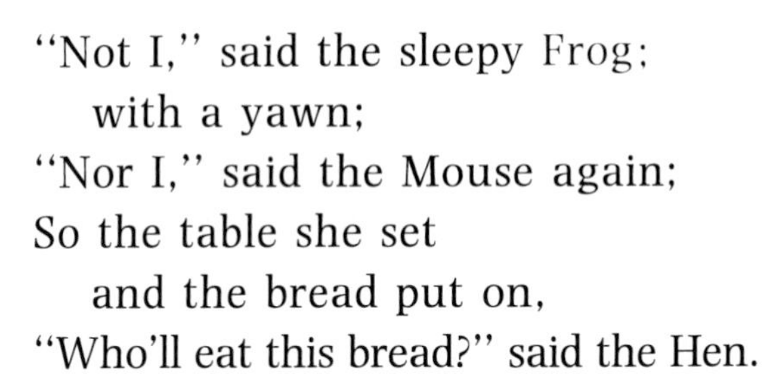

"Not I," said the sleepy Frog;
with a yawn;
"Nor I," said the Mouse again;
So the table she set
and the bread put on,
"Who'll eat this bread?" said the Hen.

"I will!" cried the Frog;
"And I!" squeaked the Mouse,
As they near the table drew:
"Oh, no, you won't!" said the Little Red Hen,
And away with the loaf she flew.

Old Mother Hubbard
Went to her cupboard,
To fetch her poor dog a bone;
But when she got there
The cupboard was bare
And so the poor dog had none.

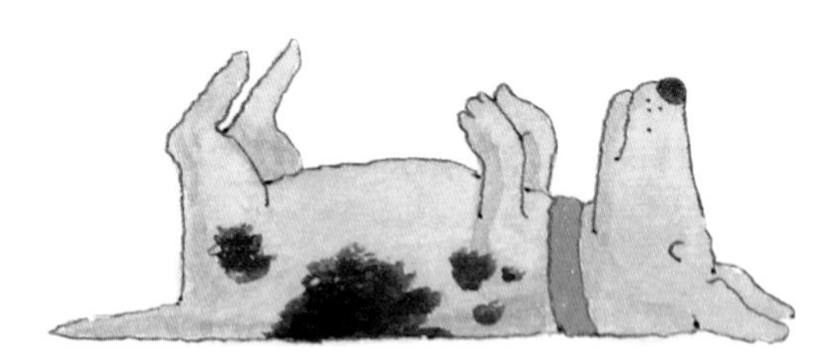

She went to the baker's
To buy him some bread;
But when she came back
The poor dog was dead.

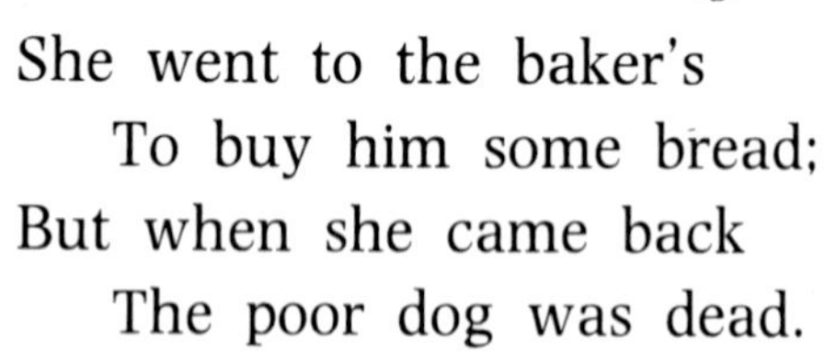

She went to the joiner's
To buy him a coffin;
But when she came back
The poor dog was laughing.

She went to the cobbler's
To buy him some shoes;
But when she came back
He was reading the news.

She went to the tailor's
  To buy him a coat;
But when she came back
  He was riding a goat.

She went to the hatter's
  To buy him a hat;
But when she came back
  He was feeding the cat.

She went to the hosier's
  To buy him some hose;
But when she came back
  He was dressed in his clothes.

The dame made a curtsey,
  The dog made a bow;
The dame said, "Your servant,"
  The dog said, "Bow-wow."

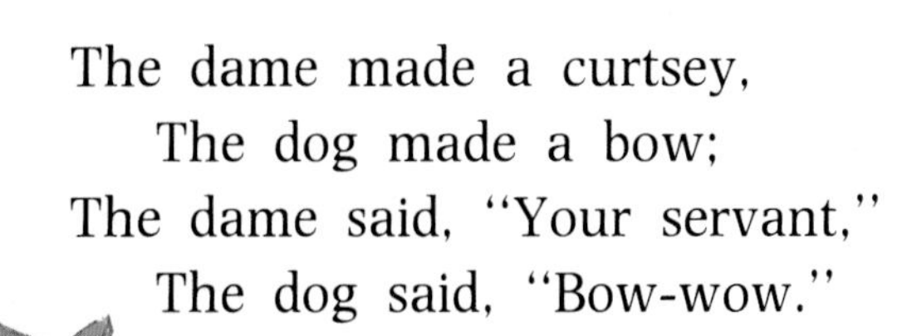

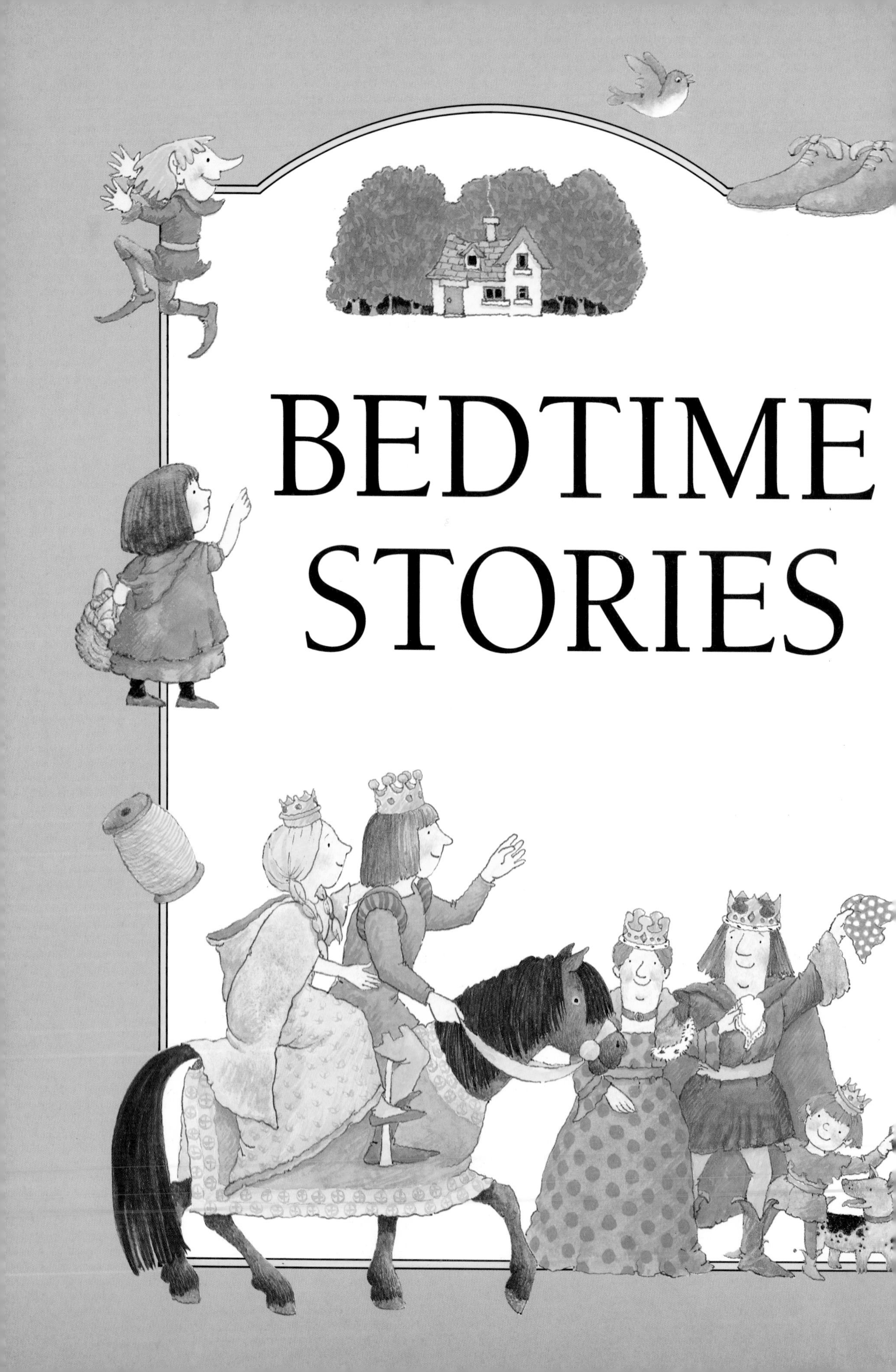

BEDTIME STORIES

The Frog Prince
204

The Elves and the Shoemaker
209

Little Red Riding Hood
216

Rumpelstiltskin
222

The Frog Prince

Once upon a time there lived a princess whose favourite toy was a golden ball. Every day she would go into the gardens of her father's palace and play with her golden ball. And every day, as she played, two big frog eyes would rise up out of the water of the palace well and watch her. But the princess did not know this.

Then one day, as the princess stretched out her hands to catch her golden ball, it slipped through her fingers. Across the grass it bounced and PLOP! into the waters of the deep, deep well it went.

How the princess cried! Tears ran down her cheeks until, through her sobs, she heard a small voice say, "Don't cry, Princess. If I get you back your ball, what will you give me in return?"

And there, looking at her with his big sad eyes, was a very large frog.

"Oh, anything, anything!" cried the princess. "Would you like jewels or gold?"

"All I want," said the frog, "is to be your companion. I should like to play with you, to eat with you at your table and to sleep in your bed at night."

"Oh, I promise, I promise!" cried the princess. No sooner had she given her word than the frog dived down into the waters of the deep, deep well and returned with the ball.

But the princess – who secretly thought frogs were nasty, slimy creatures – had no intention of keeping her promise. She snatched the ball and ran back to the palace, leaving the poor frog behind.

That night, as the princess sat eating her supper, there was the sound of a splish, splash, splosh outside the door and a small voice said:

"Great King's Daughter, open the door to me.

Remember the promise that you once gave to me."

"What promise is that?" asked the king, and the princess, feeling very ashamed of herself, told her father the story of the lost ball.

"Then you must keep your promise," said the king. "The frog shall be your companion and eat at table with you and sleep in your bed at night."

Well there was no escape. Much as she disliked the wet, green creature, the princess had to do as she was told and the frog hopped up on to the table beside her.

Later when she went off to bed, the frog followed her up the stairs. But as soon as the princess was alone with him in her bedroom where no one could see them, she picked up the frog and threw him across the room.

"Did you really think I'd let a thing like you sleep in my bed?" she cried.

The frog lay motionless on the floor, his great sad eyes watching her. And suddenly the princess was filled with sorrow.

"Oh, Frog," she cried, "I'm so sorry – I didn't mean to hurt you." She picked up the little creature, stroked him and kissed his poor wet face.

And what happened? Hey presto! The frog disappeared and in his place stood a handsome young prince.

"A wicked witch turned me into a frog," he said. "Only the love of a princess could free me from the spell."

Well of course the princess was astonished – but very pleased – and it wasn't long before she agreed to marry the handsome young prince and travel with him to his own land and live with him in his palace.

So the Frog Prince's wish came true after all. He was able to be the princess's dear companion and live with her for the rest of his life.

The Elves and the Shoemaker

Once upon a time there was a poor shoemaker. He was a good shoemaker, but there were many other shoemakers in the town and, no matter how hard he worked, he couldn't sell enough shoes to feed his family. Soon he had only one small piece of leather left and no money to buy any more.

"Without leather I can't make shoes," he said to his wife. "And if I can't make shoes, I can't sell any. And if I don't sell any shoes, we shan't have any money and we shan't be able to buy food. We shall go hungry, you and our children and I."

"Don't give up hope," said his wife. "You have this last little bit of leather, enough to make one more pair of shoes. Make that one pair to keep your mind off your worries. You never know, something may turn up to save us."

The shoemaker didn't think so, but he did as his wife said and cut one last pair of shoes out of his last piece of leather. He didn't have time to sew the shoes together that night so he left the pieces lying on his workbench. In the morning, he

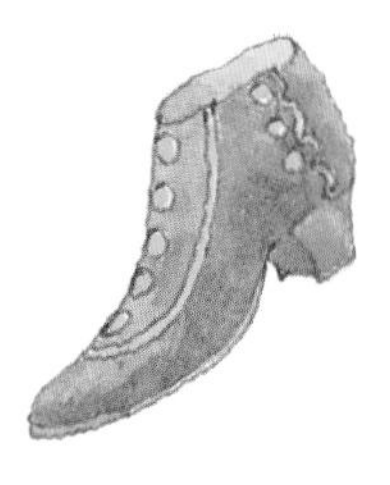

thought, he would sew them together and see if he could sell them.

But the next morning, when he came back to his workbench to finish making the shoes, he found that the pieces of leather had already been sewn together! There on the workbench stood a most beautiful pair of shoes! The shoemaker picked them up and looked at them. The stitches were so tiny they were almost invisible. The seams were so smooth they would never rub. They were the best pair of shoes he had ever seen.

"But how did they get here?" the shoemaker asked himself. "Who can have made them?"

But since the shoes *were* there and since they were so fine, the shoemaker could think of nothing better than to put them in pride of place in his

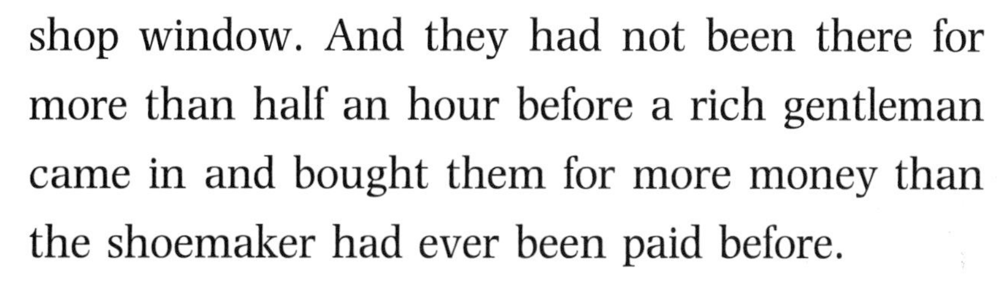

shop window. And they had not been there for more than half an hour before a rich gentleman came in and bought them for more money than the shoemaker had ever been paid before.

With the money, the shoemaker's wife was able to buy plenty of food for the family, and the shoemaker went out and bought more leather to make more shoes. All day long he worked, cutting out pairs of shoes. That night he left all the cut-out pieces on his workbench, ready to sew in the morning, and went to bed, tired out.

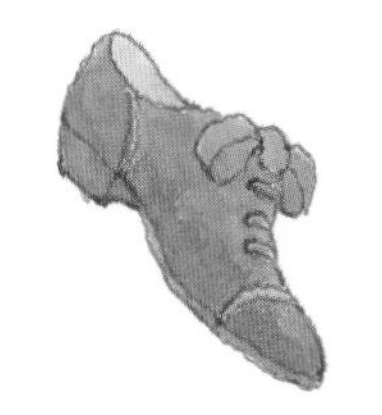

But the next morning, when the shoemaker came down to his workbench, he found that all his work had been done for him again! All the pieces he had left on his bench the night before had been sewn together, much more cleverly than the shoemaker himself could have done it. The shoemaker put the shoes in his window and by that night he had sold them all, for good prices.

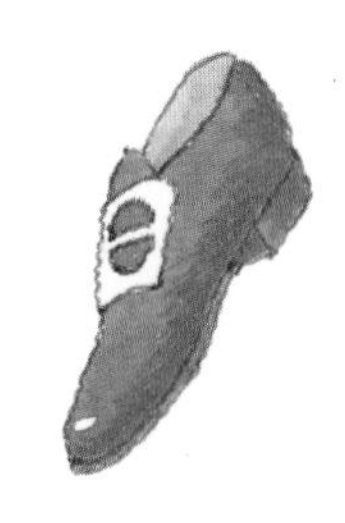

And so it went on. The shoemaker cut out shoes during the day, and during the night someone came and sewed them together. The shoemaker didn't know who was doing the

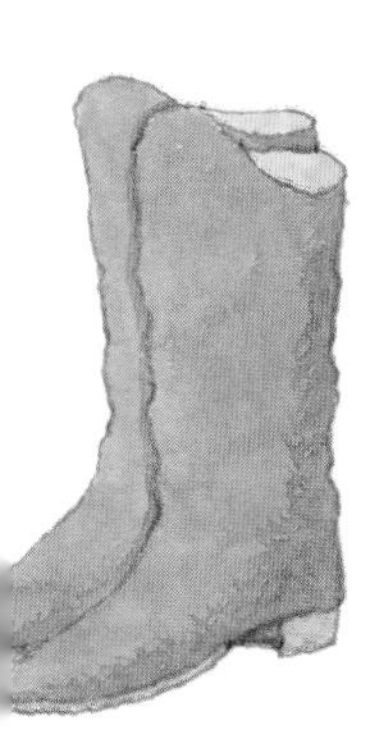

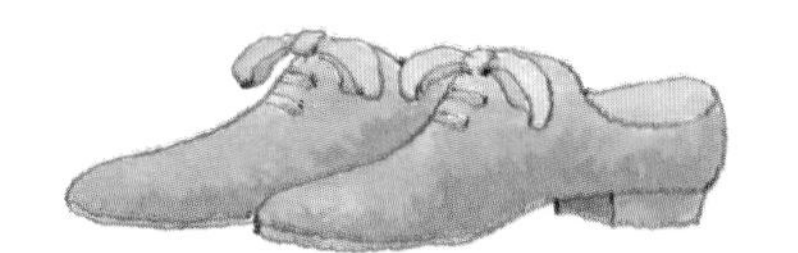

work, but, whoever it was, there wasn't a better shoemaker in town.

Soon everyone was coming to his shop to buy their shoes. The shoemaker was famous. And he was rich.

Just before Christmas the shoemaker had an idea.

"Wife," he said, "don't you think it would be a good idea to stay up one night and find out who is helping us?"

His wife agreed. So that night, instead of going to bed, they hid in the workroom and they waited to see who it was that sewed the shoes.

As the clock struck midnight, there was a sound of tiny feet, like the sound that mice make. But it wasn't mice that came running across the floor – it was two tiny men. They climbed up the legs of the workbench and set to work on the pieces of leather. The needles were as big as they were and the reels of thread were a lot bigger.

"Elves!" the shoemaker whispered. "Elves have been helping us." And he didn't know whether to be pleased or afraid; because elves are tricky creatures, you never know if they will do you a good or a bad turn.

"Poor little things," said his wife. "They haven't a stitch on. They must be cold. Husband, let's make them some clothes!"

The shoemaker thought this was an excellent idea. So the next day, the shoemaker's wife went out and bought material to make the elves some clothes. She didn't have to buy very

much, but she bought the best velvets and silks she could find. For the whole of that week she cut and sewed, working hard to make the finest little suits with the neatest, tiniest stitches. Little velvet jackets and breeches, tiny silk shirts and stockings she made, while the shoemaker used the softest leather to make two pairs of tiny little shoes.

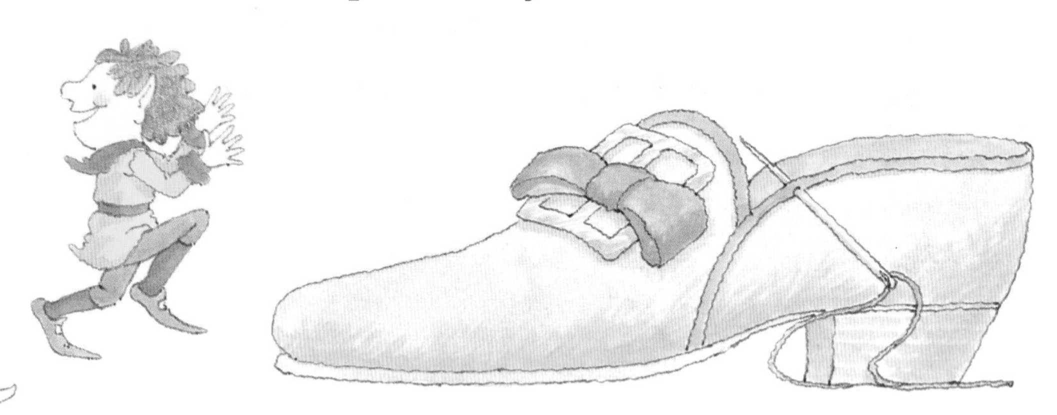

On Christmas Eve they finished the gifts, wrapped them up and left them on the workbench. Then they hid and waited to see what the elves would say when they found their presents.

At midnight, the elves came running across the floor and climbed the legs of the workbench, just as before. They were very surprised to see the tiny parcels, but it wasn't long before they had unwrapped them and put on the beautiful clothes.

Then they danced about on the workbench, admiring each other in their fine velvet breeches and soft silk shirts.

"Why, Brother," said one elf, "we can't work at a greasy old shoemaker's bench in velvet and silk!"

"I shall never work again!" said the other. "Not now I'm so fine!" And with that the two little elves jumped down from the workbench and ran away. They never came back to the shoemaker's shop, and they have never been seen anywhere else either.

But by now the shoemaker was so famous for his wonderful shoes that he still did good business. No one noticed that his stitches were not quite so tiny nor his seams so smooth, and he and his family were never poor again.

Little Red Riding Hood

Once upon a time there was a dark forest where wolves and bears lived. It was easy to get lost in that forest.

Close to the forest lived a poor woodcutter and his wife. They had one little girl and they loved her very much. They called her Little Red Riding Hood, because she always wore a hooded cloak that her granny had made for her, and it was as red as poppies or holly berries.

Little Red Riding Hood's granny lived on the other side of the forest. One day, Little Red Riding Hood's mother put some cakes and bread into a basket and said, "Little Red Riding Hood, take these things through the forest to your granny. But make sure you keep to the path so that you don't get lost. And don't stop to talk to *anyone*. Go straight there and come straight back."

"I will," said Little Red Riding Hood.

She set off through the dark forest in her bright red cloak and hood, carrying the basket.

She hadn't gone very far when she saw some flowers growing by the path. She decided to pick some for her granny. Then she saw some even bigger, prettier flowers growing among the trees and she left the path to pick them as well.

While she was picking flowers, a wolf came by.

"Good day, Little Red Riding Hood," said the wolf. "How are you?"

Her mother had said not to talk to anyone, but Little Red Riding Hood didn't think a wolf *was* anyone, and so she said, "I'm very well, thank you. How are you?"

"I'm as well as can be expected when I'm so hungry," said the wolf. "That basket looks heavy. Where are you taking it?"

"I'm taking some food to my granny, who lives on the other side of the forest," said Little Red Riding Hood.

The wolf licked his chops. "If I'm clever," he thought, "I'll be able to eat this little girl *and* her granny." So he

said, "It'll take you a long time to get to your granny's if you follow that twisty path. I know a shortcut through the trees. Come with me and I'll show you."

"No, I can't come with you and I'd better go back to the path," said Little Red Riding Hood. "My mother told me not to leave the path. You shouldn't ever leave the path when you are in the forest. Don't you know that, Wolf?"

"Oh, you'll be safe with me," said the wolf. "Come with me and I'll take you the quick way to your granny's."

"No," said Little Red Riding Hood, and she went back to the path with her basket and her flowers.

"Never mind," thought the wolf. "I'll just run ahead to her granny's and wait for her there."

And off he ran through the trees. Little Red Riding Hood went on her way along the path.

But the way through the trees was shorter, so the wolf reached granny's house first.

He knocked on the door with his paw. From inside Granny called, "Who's there?"

The wolf made his voice sweet and soft and gentle, as wolves can when they want to.

"It's your granddaughter, Little Red Riding Hood, come to see you," he said.

"Then lift up the latch and walk in," Granny called. But when the door opened, in came the hungry forest wolf and ate Granny up.

The wolf licked his chops. Then he dressed himself in Granny's nightdress and nightcap and climbed into Granny's bed. He pulled the bedclothes right up to his chin and waited for Little Red Riding Hood.

Little Red Riding Hood came walking up the forest path to her granny's house and knocked on the door. From inside came a soft, sweet, gentle voice: "Who's there?"

"It's me, Granny!" said Little Red Riding Hood.

"Then lift up the latch and walk in."

Little Red Riding Hood opened the door and went in.

Little Red Riding Hood stood at the end of Granny's bed and said, "Oh, Granny, what big eyes you have!"

"All the better to see you with," said the wolf.

"Oh, but Granny, what big ears you have!"

"All the better to hear you with."

"Oh, but Granny, what big teeth you have!"

"All the better to eat you with!" said the wolf and jumped out of bed. Off fell the nightdress, off fell the nightcap, and Little Red Riding Hood saw that it was not Granny but the wolf! She hit the wolf with her basket and shouted for help as loudly as she could.

Outside in the forest, Little Red Riding Hood's father was at work, chopping wood. He heard Little Red Riding Hood shouting and ran to see what the matter was. When he opened the door, he saw Little Red Riding Hood fighting with the wolf. With one blow of his axe he cut off the wolf's head, and out came Granny! She hugged and kissed Little Red Riding Hood, and hugged and kissed her father.

And Little Red Riding Hood never talked to wolves or left the path again.

Rumpelstiltskin

There was once a woman who baked nine pies and put them in her pantry to cool while she went to fetch some water. When she came back she found that her daughter had eaten all nine pies!

"Well!" said the woman. And to tease her daughter she made up a song:

"My daughter ate nine pies today!
My daughter ate nine pies today!"

As she was singing, the king rode by on his way to the castle. He stopped and said, "What was that song you were singing?"

The woman blushed; she was ashamed to admit that her daughter was so greedy. So she said, "Oh, Sire, I was just singing that my daughter spun nine skeins today."

"Nine skeins?" said the king. "Very good."

"Yes, Sire," the woman boasted. "And they were all gold!"

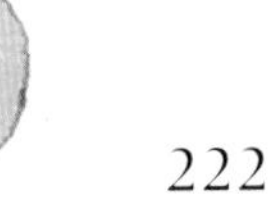

"Nine *gold* skeins?" said the king.

"Yes, and she spun them from straw!"

"Straw into gold!" exclaimed the king. "Where is your daughter? I shall marry her at once."

The woman fetched her daughter out of the house, and the king took her straight to his castle and married her that very day.

The girl was wonderfully happy at being married to the king. She was queen and could have anything she wanted – a gold ring, a gold necklace, pretty dresses, anything.

But, three days after the wedding, the king took her to a room at the top of a stone tower. The room was filled with bales of straw. There was nothing else in it except a stool and a spinning wheel.

"I need some gold for my treasury," said the king. "Spin this straw into gold, Wife."

The girl was terrified. "I might not be able to spin *all* this straw into gold, Sire . . ."

"All of it," said the king. "By tomorrow morning, or I'll chop off your head!" And out he went, locking the door behind him. The poor girl sat down on the stool and started to cry.

Then a voice said, "Tears won't spin straw into gold, but I can."

The girl looked up and saw a little man. He had long hair and a long beard and he wore a red cap.

"Who are you?" she asked.

"Never mind who I am. Do you want my help?"

"Oh, yes please!" said the girl.

"What will you give me?" asked the little man.

"I'll give you this gold ring," said the girl. She pulled the ring off her finger and held it out to him.

"That will do," he said, and he sat down at the spinning wheel and started to spin. The girl sat on a straw bale and watched him work. Soon he needed the bale she was sitting on, so she sat on a pile of gold thread instead. Long before morning every bit of straw had been spun into gold. The little man got up off the stool, jumped out of the window and was gone.

When the king unlocked the door a few hours later, he was delighted with all his gold. But he wanted more. The next night, he took the girl to the same room, but this time there was an even bigger pile of straw.

"Now, spin the whole lot into gold by morning," he said, "or I'll chop off your head!" And out he went, locking the door behind him.

The little girl began to cry again; but not for long, for the little man appeared once more.

"If I spin this second load of straw into gold, what will you give me?" he asked.

"My necklace," said the girl.

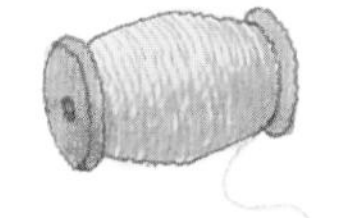

"That will do," said the little man. He sat down at the spinning wheel and long before morning he had spun every scrap of straw into gold thread. Away through the window he went, with the queen's necklace.

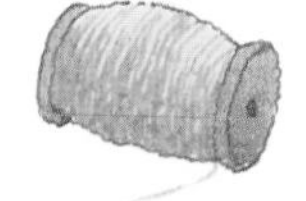

When the king saw the roomful of gold in the morning, he said, "One more night's work, Wife, and we shall have enough gold to last us forever." And once again he had the room filled with straw and locked the girl inside.

That night the girl didn't cry. She was sure the little man would come again, and so he did.

"What will you give me this time?" he asked.

"I have no more rings or necklaces," said the girl. "But do the spinning and tomorrow I'll be able to pay you anything you like."

"Tomorrow's no good to me," the little man said. "We must fix a price tonight."

"What would you like?"

The little man grinned. "I would like," he said, "your first-born child. Promise!"

Well, the queen had no children so she didn't think this was much to promise. "Alright," she said. "I promise. My first-born child shall be yours."

"I shall come to fetch it," said the little man. "But now – to work!" And he sat down at the spinning wheel and began to spin the dry straw into shining gold. By morning the room was full of gleaming gold thread.

"Remember your promise!" said the little man and leaped out of the window.

At last the king was happy. "No more spinning," he said. Now the girl could enjoy being queen again. In fact, as time went by she was so busy enjoying herself that she forgot all about the little man and the promise she had made him.

She was happier still when, a year later, her first baby was born. But that night, as she lay in bed with her baby in its cradle beside her, the little man with the

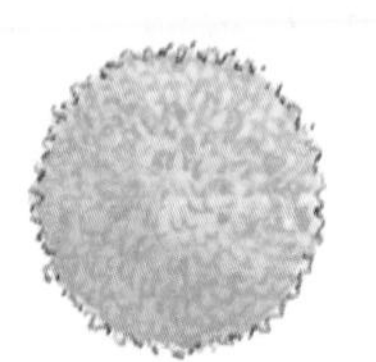

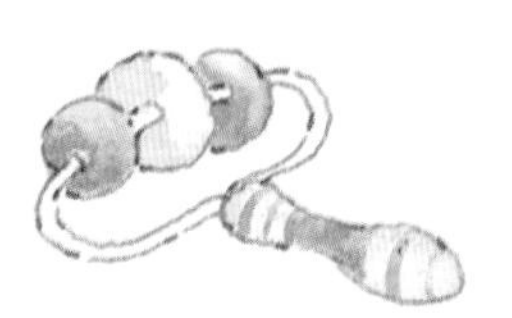

long hair and beard and the red cap jumped in through the window.

"Here I am! I've come to fetch my baby!"

The queen snatched her baby from the cradle.

"Have you forgotten your promise?" said the little man. "The baby is mine."

"No!" cried the queen. "You can have anything else, but not my baby."

"I don't want anything else," said the little man. "Only the baby."

The queen knelt and pleaded with the little man. He seemed to feel sorry for her because he said, "I will let you keep your baby, on one condition – you must guess my name. I'll give you three days, but if you can't guess, you must give me the baby. Do you agree to that?"

"Oh yes, yes!" said the queen. She knew she had no choice.

"Guess away then."

The queen sat down on the edge of her bed with her baby in her arms. She began to try to guess the little man's name.

"Is your name Peter?" she asked.

"No," said the little man.

"Is it Hans?"

"No."

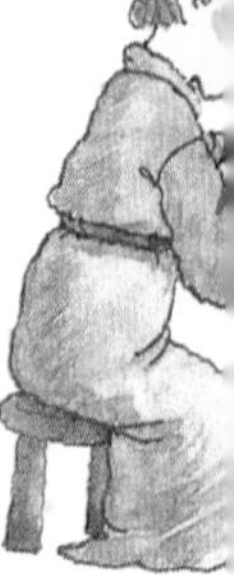

"Is it David?"

"No."

On and on the guessing went, all night long, but to all the queen's guesses the little man answered, "No". And when morning came, he leaped out of the window.

The queen called together all the cleverest people in the kingdom and asked them to write down all the boys' names they could think of. In case there were names even those clever people didn't know, she also sent messengers out to every corner of the kingdom to write down the names of every man they met.

When the little man came back on the second night, the queen had sheets and sheets of paper by

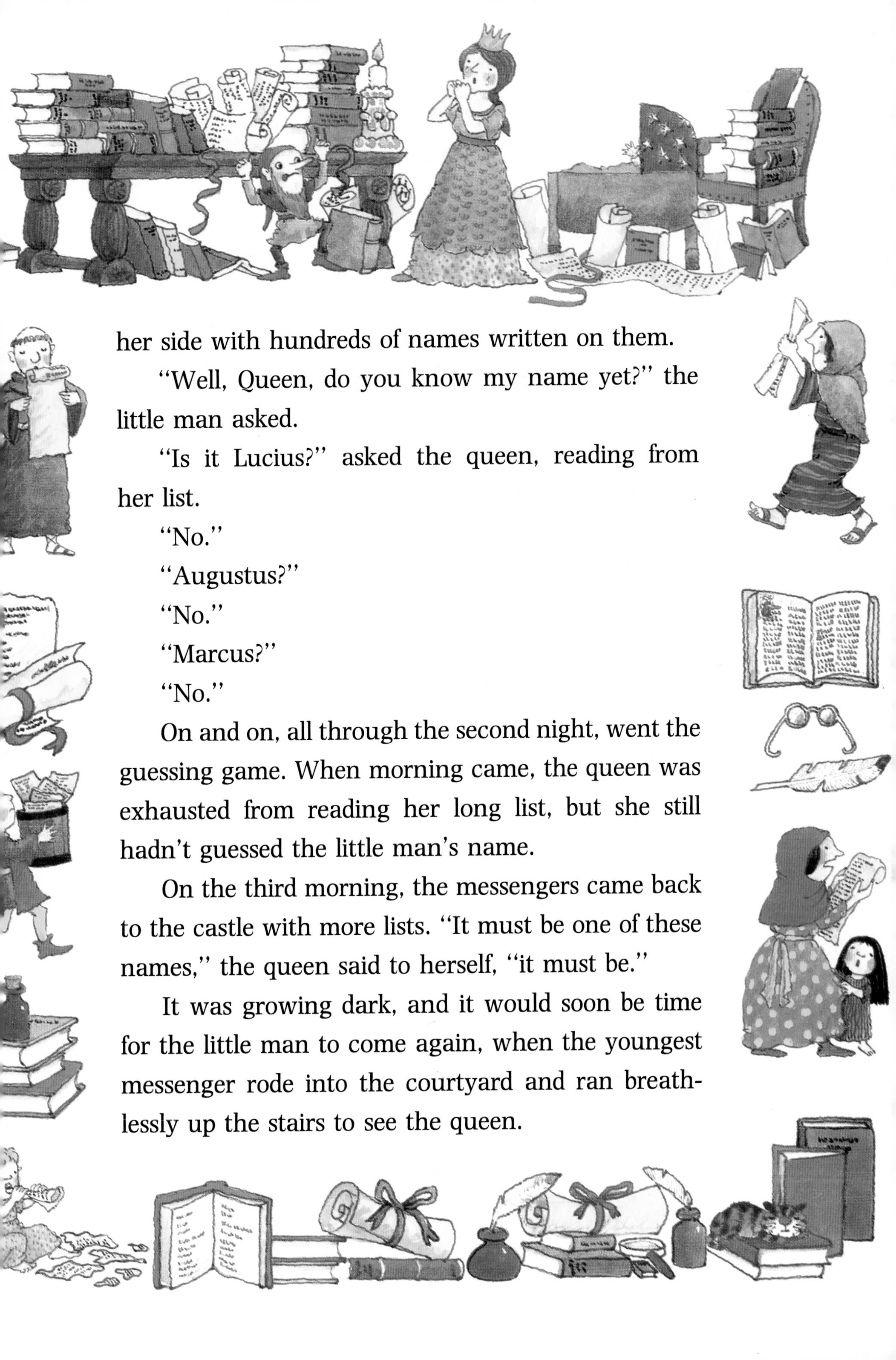

her side with hundreds of names written on them.

"Well, Queen, do you know my name yet?" the little man asked.

"Is it Lucius?" asked the queen, reading from her list.

"No."

"Augustus?"

"No."

"Marcus?"

"No."

On and on, all through the second night, went the guessing game. When morning came, the queen was exhausted from reading her long list, but she still hadn't guessed the little man's name.

On the third morning, the messengers came back to the castle with more lists. "It must be one of these names," the queen said to herself, "it must be."

It was growing dark, and it would soon be time for the little man to come again, when the youngest messenger rode into the courtyard and ran breathlessly up the stairs to see the queen.

"Your Majesty, as I was riding through a dark forest, I saw a fire. When I came close, I saw a little man dancing around the fire."

"Did he have long hair and a long beard and a red cap?" asked the queen.

"Yes, Your Majesty. And as he danced, he sang, and this is what he sang:

'First I brew, then I bake,

Tomorrow the queen's child I'll take;

At guessing my name she'll never win,

For it is RUMPELSTILTSKIN!'

"Rumpelstiltskin!" said the queen. "Is that a name?"

"It's the strangest name I've ever heard," said the messenger, "but that is what he sang."

The queen rewarded the boy with a precious ring and waited for the little man.

He appeared, grinning. "One last chance, Queen," he said. "And when you can't guess my name, I shall take away my baby!"

"Oh!" said the queen, pretending to be afraid. "Is your name Finn?"

"No." And the little man grinned again.

"Is it Jerome?"

"No." And the little man laughed.

The sun was coming up and the sky began to grow lighter. The little man leaned over the baby's cradle.

"Is it . . . is it Rumpelstiltskin?"

The little man stood with his mouth open. "Yes," he said.

"Then I keep my baby!" said the queen. The little man flung down his cap in rage, leaped forward from the window and was never seen again.

And that is the end of the story, except to say that the queen and her baby lived happily ever after and the queen named her baby – guess what?

LULLABIES

The Man in the Moon *234*
Wee Willie Winkie *234*
Niddledy, noddledy *235*
Lie abed *235*
Twinkle, twinkle, little star *236*
Star light, star bright *236*
Hush-a-bye, don't you cry *237*
Hush thee, my babby *237*
Bye low, bye low *238*
Golden Slumbers *238*
Where should a baby rest? *239*
Sleepy time *239*
Love Me *240*
Hush-a-bye baby *240*
Brahms' Lullaby *241*
Hush, little baby, don't say a word *242*
A Chill *244*
Sleep, baby, sleep *245*
The White Seal's Lullaby *245*
Kum Ba Yah *246*
Scarborough Fair *247*
Sweet and Low *248*
A Baby's Boat *249*

The Man in the Moon looked
out of the moon,
Looked out of the moon
and said:
'Tis time for all children
on the earth
To think about going to bed!

Wee Willie Winkie runs through the town,
Upstairs and downstairs in his nightgown,
Rapping at the window, crying through the lock:
Are all the children in their beds, it's past eight o'clock?

Niddledy, noddledy,
To and fro.
Tired and sleepy,
To bed we go.

Jump into bed,
Switch out the light,
Head on the pillow,
Shut your eyes tight.

Lie abed,
Sleepy head,
Shut up eyes, bo-peep;
Till day-break
Never wake;
Baby sleep.

Twinkle, twinkle, little star,
How I wonder what you are!
Up above the world so high,
Like a diamond in the sky.

Then the traveller in the dark
Thanks you for your tiny spark;
He could not see which way to go,
If you did not twinkle so.

In the dark blue sky you keep
And often through my curtains peep,
For you never shut your eye
Till the sun is in the sky.

As your bright and tiny spark
Lights the traveller in the dark,
Though I know not what you are,
Twinkle, twinkle, little star.

Star light, star bright,
First star I see tonight,
I wish I may, I wish I might,
Have the wish I wish tonight.

Hush-a-bye, don't
you cry,
Go to sleepy,
little baby.

When you wake, you
shall have a cake
And all the pretty
little horses.

Blacks and bays,
dapples and greys,
Coach and six
white horses.

Hush thee, my babby,
Lie still with thy daddy,
Thy mammy has gone to the mill,
To get some meal
To bake a cake,
So pray, my dear babby, lie still.

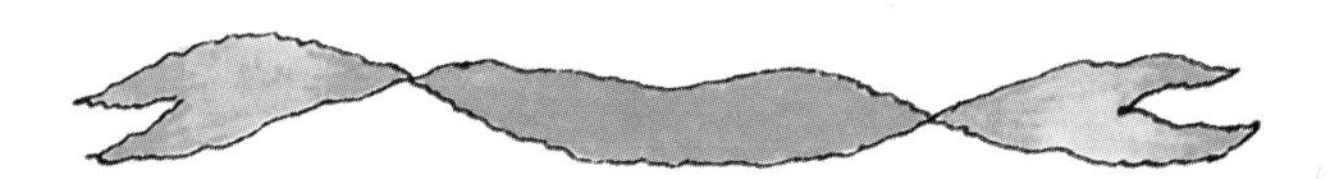

Bye low, bye low,
Baby's in the cradle sleeping;
Tip toe, tip toe,
Still as pussy slyly creeping;
Bye low, bye low,
Rock the cradle, baby's waking;
Hush, my baby, oh!

Golden Slumbers

Golden slumbers kiss your eyes,
Smiles awake you when you rise.
  Sleep, pretty wantons, do not cry,
  And I will sing a lullaby:
Rock them, rock them, lullaby.

Care is heavy, therefore sleep you;
You are care and care must keep you.
  Sleep, pretty wantons, do not cry,
  And I will sing a lullaby:
Rock them, rock them, lullaby.

THOMAS DECKER

Where should a baby rest?
Where but on its mother's arm –
Where can a baby lie
Half so safe from every harm?
Lulla, lulla, lullaby,
Softly sleep, my baby;
Lulla, lulla, lullaby,
Soft, soft, my baby.

Sleepy time has come
for my baby,
Baby now is going to sleep;
Kiss Mama good night and
we'll turn out the light,
While I tuck you in beneath
your covers tight;
Sleepy time has come
for my baby,
Baby now is going to sleep.

Love Me

Love me, – I love you,
  Love me, my baby;
Sing it high, sing it low,
  Sing it as may be.

Mother's arms under you,
  Her eyes above you
Sing it high, sing it low,
  Love me, – I love you.

CHRISTINA ROSSETTI

Hush-a-bye baby
On the tree top.
When the wind blows,
The cradle will rock;
When the bough breaks,
The cradle will fall;
Down will come baby,
Cradle and all.

Brahms' Lullaby

Lullaby and goodnight,
With lilies of white
And roses of red
To pillow your head:
May you wake when the day
Chases darkness away,
May you wake when the day
Chases darkness away.

Lullaby and goodnight,
Let angels of light
Spread wings round your bed
And guard you from dread.
Slumber gently and deep
In the dreamland of sleep,
Slumber gently and deep
In the dreamland of sleep.

JOHANNES BRAHMS

Hush, little baby, don't say a word,
Papa's gonna buy you a mocking bird.

If that mocking bird won't sing,
Papa's gonna buy you a diamond ring.

If the diamond ring turns to brass,
Papa's gonna buy you a looking glass.

If that looking glass gets broke,
Papa's gonna buy you a billy goat.

If that billy goat won't pull,
Papa's gonna buy you a cart and a bull.

If that cart and bull turn over,
Papa's gonna buy you a dog named Rover.

If that dog named Rover won't bark,
Papa's gonna buy you a horse and cart,

If that horse and cart fall down,
You'll still be the sweetest baby in town.

A Chill

What can lambkins do,
All the keen night through?
Nestle by their woolly mother,
The careful ewe.

What can nestlings do,
In the nightly dew?
Sleep beneath their mother's wing,
Till day breaks anew.

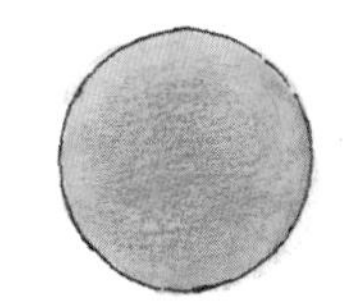

If in field or tree,
There might only be,
Such a warm, soft, sleep place,
Found for me!

CHRISTINA ROSSETTI

Sleep, baby, sleep.
Thy father guards the sheep;
Thy mother shakes the dreamland tree,
Down falls a little dream for thee:
Sleep, baby, sleep.

The White Seal's Lullaby

Oh! hush thee, my baby, the night is behind us,
  And black are the waters that sparkled so green.
The moon o'er the combers, looks downward to find us
  At rest in the hollows that rustle between.
Where billow meets billow, then soft be thy pillow;
  Ah, weary wee flipperling, curl at thy ease,
The storm shall not wake thee, nor shark overtake thee,
  Asleep in the arms of the slow-swinging seas.

RUDYARD KIPLING

Kum Ba Yah

Kum ba yah, my Lord, kum ba yah,
Kum ba yah, my Lord, kum ba yah,
Kum ba yah, my Lord, kum ba yah,
Oh Lord, kum ba yah.

Someone's singing, Lord, kum ba yah,
Someone's singing, Lord, kum ba yah,
Someone's singing, Lord, kum ba yah,
Oh Lord, kum ba yah.

Scarborough Fair

Are you going to Scarborough Fair?
Sing parsley, sage, rosemary and thyme.
Remember me to one who lives there,
For once she was a true love of mine.

Tell her to buy me an acre of land,
Sing parsley, sage, rosemary and thyme.
Beneath the wild ocean and yonder sea strand,
And she shall be a true love of mine.

Tell her to make me a cambric shirt,
Sing parsley, sage, rosemary and thyme.
Without any stitching or needlework,
And she shall be a true love of mine.

Tell her to wash it in yonder dry well,
Sing parsley, sage, rosemary and thyme.
Where water ne'er sprung, nor a drop of rain fell,
And she shall be a true love of mine.

Tell her to dry it on yonder sharp thorn,
Sing parsley, sage, rosemary and thyme.
Which never bore blossom since Adam was born,
And she shall be a true love of mine.

Sweet and Low

Sweet and low, sweet and low,
  Wind of the western sea.
Low, low, breathe and blow,
  Wind of the western sea!
  Over the rolling waters go,
  Come from the dying moon,
  and blow,
  Blow him again to me;
While my little one, while my
  pretty one, sleeps.

Sleep and rest, sleep and rest,
  Father will come to thee soon;
Rest, rest, on mother's breast,
  Father will come to thee soon;
  Father will come to his babe
  in the nest,
  Silver sails all out of the west
  Under the silver moon;
Sleep, my little one, my pretty
  one, sleep.

ALFRED, LORD TENNYSON

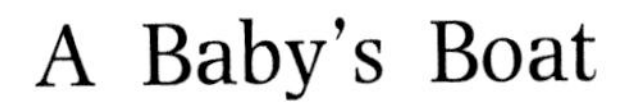

A Baby's Boat

Baby's boat's a silver moon
Sailing in the sky,
Sailing o'er a sea of sleep
While the stars float by.

Sail, baby, sail
Out upon that sea;
Only don't forget to sail
Back again to me.

Baby's fishing for a dream,
Fishing far and near,
Her line a silver moonbeam is.
Her bait a silver star.

Sail, baby, sail
Out upon that sea;
Only don't forget to sail
Back again to me.

INDEX

American jump! American jump! *125*
Are you going to Scarborough Fair? *247*
A trot, a canter *31*
A was an apple pie *168*
A was an archer *178*
A wise old owl sat in an oak *175*

Baa, baa, black sheep *82*
Baby's boat's a silver moon *249*
Bobby Shaftoe's gone to sea *86*
Bow-wow, says the dog *183*
Bye low, bye low *238*

Can you keep a secret? *14*
Can you walk on tiptoe? *123*
Christmas is coming *83*
Cuckoo, cuckoo, what do you do? *177*

Dance, Thumbkin, dance *16*
Dance to your daddy *25*
Ding, dong, bell *72*
Doctor Foster went to Gloucester *74*

Father and Mother and Uncle John *22*
Five brown teddies sitting on a wall *170*
Five little monkeys walked along the shore *182*
Frère Jacques, Frère Jacques *136*

Georgie Porgie, pudding and pie *73*
Girls and boys, come out to play *89*
Golden slumbers kiss your eyes *238*
Goosey, goosey gander *84*
Go to bed late *175*

Handy Pandy *20*
Handy Pandy, Jack-a-dandy *124*
Head and shoulders, knees and toes *120*
Here am I *124*
Here are the lady's knives and forks *15*
Here is a ball for baby *26*

Here sits Farmer Giles *12*
Here we go looby-loo *140*
Here we go round the mulberry bush *127*
Hey diddle, diddle *88*
Hickety, pickety, my black hen *84*
Hickory, dickory, dock *71*
Hob, shoe, hob *21*
Hot cross buns! Hot cross buns! *80*
Humpty Dumpty sat on a wall *66*
Hush-a-bye baby *240*
Hush-a-bye don't you cry *237*
Hush, little baby, don't say a word *242*
Hush thee, my babby *237*

I can tie my shoelaces *134*
If you're happy and you know it *120*
I had a little nut tree *80*
I hear thunder, I hear thunder *137*
I love little pussy *72*
I'm a little teapot *134*
Incey Wincey spider *85*
I sent a letter to my love *141*
It's raining, it's pouring *74*

Jack and Jill *187*
Jack be nimble *124*
Jack-in-the-box *30*
Jack Sprat could eat no fat *79*
Jelly on the plate *24*
Jingle, bells! Jingle, bells! *83*

Knock at the door *14*
Kum ba yah, my Lord, kum ba yah *246*

Ladybird, ladybird *68*
Lavender's blue, dilly, dilly *69*
Leg over leg *21*
Lie abed *235*
Little Bo-peep has lost her sheep *196*
Little Boy Blue *68*
Little Jack Horner *83*
Little Miss Muffet *197*
London Bridge is falling down *133*
Love me – I love you *240*
Lullaby and goodnight *241*

Mackerel sky *174*
Manners in the dining-room *175*

Mary had a little lamb *186*
Mary, Mary, quite contrary *82*
Miss Polly had a dolly *128*
Monday's child is fair of face *176*
Mr East gave a feast *177*

Niddledy, noddledy *235*

O dear, what can the matter be? *87*
Oh, do you know the muffin man *78*
Oh! hush thee, my baby, the night is behind us *245*
Oh, the grand old Duke of York *122*
Oh, we can play on the big bass drum *129*
Old King Cole was a merry old soul *67*
Old Macdonald had a farm *70*
Old Mother Hubbard *200*
Once a Mouse, a Frog, and a Little Red Hen *198*
One day I went to sea *128*
One for sorrow *183*
One misty, moisty morning *74*
One, two *172*
1, 2, 3, 4 *171*
One, two, three, four, five *171*
Oranges and lemons *132*

Pat-a-cake, pat-a-cake, baker's man *20*
Pease porridge hot *79*
Peter, Peter, pumpkin eater *81*
Polly put the kettle on *78*
Pussy cat, pussy cat *193*

Rain, rain, go away *75*
Red sky at night *175*
Ride a cock-horse to Banbury Cross *31*
Rigadoon, rigadoon *25*
Ring-a-ring o' roses *28*
Rock, rock, rock your boat *31*
Round and round the garden *27*
Round and round the rugged rock *126*
Rub-a-dub-dub *75*

Sally go round the sun *130*
See a pin and pick it up *174*
See-saw, Margery Daw *130*
Sing a song of sixpence *76*
Sleep, baby, sleep *245*
Sleepy time has come for my baby *239*
Star light, star bright *236*
Stepping over stepping stones *126*

Sweet and low,
sweet and low 248
Swing me low 130

Teddybear, teddybear 121
The cock does crow 174
The elephant goes 26
The Farmer's in the den 135
The Man in the Moon 234
The Owl and the Pussy Cat
went to sea 194
The Queen of Hearts 192
There was a little girl 81
There were five in the
bed 170
The wheels on the bus go
round and round 138
The wood was dark 131
Thirty days hath
September 177
This is the way the ladies
ride 23
This little cow eats grass 17
This little pig went to
market 19
This pig got into the barn 18
Three blind mice! Three
blind mice! 71
Three little kittens 188
Three times round went our
gallant, gallant ship 141
Tinker, tailor, soldier, sailor 171
Tom, Tom, the piper's son 73
Twinkle, twinkle, little star 236
Two little dicky birds 16

Up and down the City Road 85

Wee Wiggie 17
Wee Willie Winkie runs
through the town 234
What can lambkins do 244
What shall we do with a
lazy Katie? 29
What's your name? 131
Where are you going, you
little pig? 190
Where should a baby rest? 239

Yankee Doodle came to town 86